# THE PRACTICAL DESIGN OF STRUCTURAL ELEMENTS IN TIMBER

# The Practical Design of Structural Elements in Timber

## Second Edition

### John W Bull

Gower

Second edition published 1994 by
Gower Publishing Limited
Gower House
Croft Road
Aldershot
Hants GU11 3HR
England

Gower
Old Post Road
Brookfield
Vermont 05036
USA


**British Library Cataloguing in Publication Data**

Bull, John W.
 Practical Design of Structural Elements
 in Timber – 2 Rev. ed
 I. Title
 624.184

ISBN 0 291 39802 2

**Library of Congress Cataloguing-in-Publication Data**
Bull, John W.
 The practical design of structural elements in timber / John W.
Bull. – 2nd ed.
  p.   cm.
 Includes Index.
 ISBN 0-291-3980-2.
 1. Building. Wooden.   I. Title.
 TA666.B85   1994                                                94-7967
 624.1′84 – dc20                                                      CIP


Typeset in 11 point Baskerville by Photoprint, Torquay, Devon
and printed in Great Britain at the University Press, Cambridge.

# Contents

# Contents

# List of figures and tables

## Tables

**List of figures and tables**

# Preface

The aim of this book is to provide a practical and simplified guide to the design of structural elements in timber. The book has been specifically written for those educational establishments where timber design is taught and for those design engineers who wish to design in timber, but who are perhaps not as familiar with timber as they are with other materials, such as steel or concrete. In addition, the book has also been written for those persons who are required to check timber design calculation and who wish to ensure the calculations have considered all the relevant modification factors.

The book does not deal comprehensively with all aspects of timber construction. Readers who are regular timber designers will already be familiar with the *Timber Designers Manual* by J. A. Baird and E. C. Ozelton and *Structural Timber Design and Technology* by C. J. Mettem. Both of these books more nearly agree with the requirements of chartered civil or structural engineers, and other suitably qualified persons, who have been entrusted with the complete design of timber structures.

Timber is a natural, renewable material. It is essential that it is used efficiently and effectively. The timber designer must be aware that many hundreds of timber species and grades are available, each with their own strengths, moduli of elasticity, durability, availability, etc. Rather than design by specifying a species and grade, BS 5268: Pt 2 allocates timbers to one of nine strength classes. This eases the design process, but does not absolve the designer from the responsibility of knowing the strengths, weaknesses and durability of the timber, specified in the design.

When designing in timber, the inherent directionality of the material means that a range of modification factors have to be used. This may present the designer with problems as these modification factors are not directly comparable to the factors that may be used in structural steel or concrete design. For this reason and to give the book a down-to-earth, practical approach, many worked examples using the modification factors have been included.

The book has been logically divided into twelve chapters. The chapters cover the main areas of timber design, such as loading, beams, columns, glulam, joint, etc. with design examples being associated with eleven of the twelve chapters. The use of plywood, tempered hardboard and wood chipboard is also included.

Each chapter starts with a précis of the relevant parts, sections and clauses of BS 5268 followed by design examples. Within each chapter, where sections of other chapters are referred to, they are referenced by chapter number and section and in some cases followed by the clause number in BS 5268.

In Chapter 1, the general aspects of structural timber are discussed.

Chapter 2 sets out the way in which timber loading must be considered together with a number of design examples.

Chapters 3, 4 and 5 look at specific timber members, in this case flexural members, compression members and tension members and gives design examples for each member.

Chapters 6, 7 and 8 take three wood-based products, namely glued laminated timber, plywood and tempered hardboard and shows how each can be used as a structural material.

Timber members must be joined together and this is discussed, with examples, in Chapter 9 on joints.

Timber's reaction to treatment is another area that requires careful consideration. The increasingly wide range of available timber treatments means that the advice of the treatment manufacturers should be sought before specifying a treatment. For this reason Chapter 10 is very short and only deals with the topic in very general terms.

Chapter 11 deals with the resistance of timber to fire, which is predictable with regard to the rate of charring and loss of strength.

Chapter 12 includes the new work on chipboard as published in BS 5268: Pt 2: 1991. A design example is included in Chapter 3.

Finally, I would like to acknowledge the support of my wife, Sonia, whose idea it was that I should write the first edition of this book and to update it for the second edition, and of my son Jonathan, who always had a valid reason for wanting the word processor. I am indebted to the

British Standards Institution for their permission to reproduce extracts from BS 5268 and also from BS 6399. Copies of the standards may be obtained from BSI Sales, Linford Wood, Milton Keynes, MK14 6LE, Tel: 0908 221166. I also thank the Timber Research and Development Association (TRADA) for their help and assistance, Tel: 0494 563091.

*Eur Ing Dr John W Bull*
*BSc, PhD, FIHT, FIWSc, CEng, MIStructE MICE*

# Notation

The notation used in this book is almost the same as that used in BS 5268: Part 2. The difference between the notation in the British Standard and the notation in this book is that certain subscripts, for example those following the modification faction $K$, are not subscripts in this book. The alteration is to aid clarification.

For example $K_3$ is written as $K3$.

| Symbol | Definition |
| --- | --- |
| $a$ | Applied stress |
| $A$ | Area |
| adm | Permissible stress |
| apex | Apex |
| $b$ | Breadth or web thickness |
| $c$ | Compression (stress) |
| $d$ | Diameter/beam depth |
| $e$ | Effective (stress) |
| $E$ | Modulus of elasticity |
| $F$ | Force or load |
| $G$ | Shear modulus |
| $h$ | Beam depth/timber width |
| $i$ | Radius of gyration |
| $I$ | Section moment of area |
| $K$ | Modification factor |

| | |
|---|---|
| $m$ | Bending (stress) |
| m.c. | Moisture content |
| mean | Arithmetic mean |
| $n$ | Number |
| $Q$ | First moment of inertia |
| $r$ | Radius of curvature |
| $t$ | Thickness or tension |
| tang | Tangential |
| $V$ | Shear load |
| $W$ | Load |
| $y$ | Half beam depth |
| $\alpha$ | Angle |
| $\lambda$ | Slenderness ratio |
| $\sigma$ | Stress |
| $\tau$ | Shear stress |
| $\parallel$ | Parallel to the grain |
| $\perp$ | Perpendicular to the grain |

# British Standards referred to

It is not possible in this book to fully list all the BSI publications that relate to structural timber design. However, Table 1 lists the BSI publications most often referred to in this book and Table 2 gives the BS numbers that relate to structural timber design and are in the subject index of the BSI catalogue.

In addition to the BSI publications listed in Tables 1 and 2, BS 5268: Pt 2 also refers to additional publications not included here.

British Standards are revised by the issue of either amendments or of revised editions. It is essential that the user of the British Standard ensures that the latest edition of the BS, together with all its amendments are being used.

The 1991 edition, BS 5268: Pt 2: 1991, has been produced principally to allow for the inclusion of information on chipboard grade stresses. It also makes other minor changes; the principal change being the increasing of the glued laminated timber $E$ values given in Section 3 and to correct errors and omissions in the 1988 edition.

## Table 1    BSI publications most often referred to

| BS number | BS title |
| --- | --- |
| BS 4169 | Specification for manufacture of glued laminated timber structural members |
| BS 4471 | Specification for sizes of sawn and processed softwoods |
| BS 4978 | Specification for softwood grades for structural use |
| BS 5268: | Structural use of timber |
| Part 2 | Code of practice for permissible stress design, materials and workmanship |
| Part 3 | Code of practice for trussed rafter roofs |
| | Section 4.1: Recommendations for calculating fire resistance of timber members |
| | Section 4.2: Recommendations for calculating fire resistance of timber stud walls and joisted floor construction |
| Part 5 | Code of practice for the preservative treatments for structural timber |
| BS 5291 | Specification for manufacture of finger joints of structural softwoods |
| BS 5450 | Specification for sizes of hardwoods and methods of measurement |
| BS 5756 | Specification for tropical hardwoods graded for structural use |
| BS 5669 | Particleboard |
| BS 6399: | Loading for buildings |
| Part 1 | Code of practice for dead and imposed loads |
| Part 3 | Code of practice for imposed roof loads |
| BS 6446 | Specification for manufacture of glued structural components of timber and wood-based panel products |
| CP 3: Chapter V: | |
| Part 2 | Wind loads |
| CP 112: | Code of practice for the structural use of timber (Now withdrawn) |

## Table 2  BS numbers related to BSI catalogue subject index

| BSI subject index | BS number/CP number |
| --- | --- |
| Hardwoods | 5450, 5756 |
| Sawn timber | 4471 |
| Softwoods | 4471, 5291 |
| Structural members | 4169, 5268, 6446 |
| Structural timber | 4169, 4978, 5268, 5291, 5756, 6446, CP 112 |
| Timber connectors | 1579 |
| Wood | 373, 881, 5268, 5450, 5756, 5820, 6100 |
| Wood chipboard | 5669 |

# 1 General aspects of structural timber

## 1.1 Introduction

BS 5268: *The structural use of timber*, is published by British Standards Institution in six parts as follows:

1 Part 2, *Code of practice for permissible stress design, materials and workmanship*. This gives guidance on the structural use of timber, plywood, glued laminated timber, tempered hardboard and wood chipboard in load-bearing members. Part 2 also makes recommendations on quality, grade stress and modification factors applicable to these materials, the design of joints, workmanship, testing and maintenance.
2 Part 3, *Code of practice for trussed rafter roofs*. This part provides guidance on the design, fabrication and use of trussed rafters for pitched roofs. It is intended primarily for dwellings but it is also applicable to other buildings where the environment or service conditions are similar.
3 Part 4, *Fire resistance of timber structures*, Section 4.1 'Recommendations for calculating fire resistance of timber members'. This section provides methods of assessing the fire resistance of flexural, tension and compression members of solid or glued laminated timber and their joints.
Section 4.2 'Recommendations for calculating fire resistance of timber stud walls and joisted floor construction'. Extends Section 4.1 to include composite timber elements.

1

4   Part 5, *Code of practice for the preservative treatments for structural timber.* Gives recommendations for the treatment of timber for use in the UK to protect them from degradation by wood destroying organisms.
5   Part 6, *Code of practice for timber frame walls*, Section 6.1 'Dwellings not exceeding three storeys'.
6   Part 7, *Recommendations for the calculation basis for span tables.*

BS 5268: Parts 2 and 3 replace CP 112: *Code of practice for the structural use of timber*, Part 2: 1971, *Metric units* and Part 3: 1973, *Trussed rafters for roofs of dwellings.* Both parts of CP 112 have subsequently been withdrawn.

The Commission of the European Communities (CEC) is issuing European codes, or Eurocodes for the design and construction of buildings and civil-engineering structures. Eurocode No. 5: *Common unified rules for timber structures*, is intended to establish a set of common rules as an alternative to the different rules in force in the various member states (i.e. BS 5268: Pt 2, in the case of the United Kingdom). It is believed that Eurocode No. 5 will be available for use in the late 1990s. The present British Standard will remain.

## 1.2   Scope

In its scope, BS 5268: Pt 2 does not deal comprehensively with all aspects of timber construction, but does provide guidance on the structural use of those timbers listed in Appendix A of Part 2 (which is not an exhaustive list of structural timbers) – plywoods, glued laminated timber, tempered hardboard and wood chipboard in load-bearing members.

## 1.3   Definitions

Certain definitions frequently referred to in this book are given in Table 1.1 opposite.

## 1.4   Design considerations

BS 5268: Pt 2 design requirements may be satisfied by calculation, using the laws of structural mechanics or by load testing. It is also assumed that the design of timber structures is entrusted to chartered civil or structural engineers, or to otherwise suitably qualified persons, and that the work is carried out under qualified supervision.

2

### Table 1.1 Definitions

| Term used | Definition |
| --- | --- |
| Dry stress | Stress applicable to material exposed in a condition which would result in solid timber having a moisure content not exceeding 18 per cent in service. |
| Wet stress | Stress applicable to material exposed in conditions which would result in softwoods having a moisture content exceeding 18 per cent in service. |
| Grade stress | Stress which can be permanently sustained by material of a specific section size and of a particular strength class or species and grade. |
| Permissible stress | The product of the grade stress and the appropriate modification factors for the section size, service and loading. |
| Glued laminated member | Structural timber member with a number of laminations glued together, with the grain of the laminations essentially parallel. |
| Strength class | The classification of timber based on particular values of grade stress. |

The designer must consider the stability and robustness of the design, not only for the completed structure but also for the members and components during manufacture and construction.

The moisture content of the timber and wood-based panel products should, when installed, be as close as possible to the moisture content they will attain in service. Table 1.2 gives the average moisture content for softwoods and hardwoods for selected categories of end use. Different moisture contents apply to plywoods, hardboards and glued laminated members. (These are given in BS 5268: Pt 2, clause 5.4.) As the moisture content of the timber affects the strength properties, the permissible design stresses should be those corresponding to the service condition moisture content.

The bending, tension and compression stresses and moduli of elasticity are applicable to specific section sizes as given below.

(a) 300 mm deep (or wide for tension) if assigned to a strength class or if graded to BS 4978, BS 5756 or NLGA or NGRDL joist and plank rules.

### Table 1.2   Timber moisture content

| Timber location in building | Moisture content (%) | |
|---|---|---|
| | Average attained in service | Not to be exceeded at time of erection |
| Fully-exposed external use | 18+ | – |
| Covered and generally unheated | 18 | 24 |
| Covered and generally heated | 16 | 21 |
| Internal in continuously heated building | 14 | 19 |

Source: Reproduced with permission from BS 5268: Pt 2

(b)   89 mm deep (or wide for tension) if graded to NLGA or NGRDL structural light framing, light framing or stud rules.

(c)   The particular section size quoted if graded to the North American MSR rules.

The grade stresses are modified for section sizes other than given in (a) or (b) above. For (c), the grade stresses should not be modified for section size.

## 1.5   The strength of timber

Structural timber comes from the trunk of trees. The tree trunk consists of long, vertically-elongated fibres parallel to the trunk axis, which are required to conduct fluid upwards from the tree roots to the branches and leaves. It is these fibres (or grain) which produce different mechanical and physical properties in different directions (anisotropy) within the structural timber. The anisotropy is enhanced and compli-cated by two additional factors:

1   The rate of growth of the tree varies within each year and also from year to year, thus affecting the timber density. Generally, an increase in timber density is accompanied by an increase in timber strength.
2   The growth of branches causes knots in the tree trunk. The knots alter not only the timber density, but also the direction of the long, vertically-elongated parallel fibres.

The strength class (see Table 1.4) acknowledges the anisotropic nature of timber by giving grade stresses related to whether the timber is resisting the applied load by bending, tension, compression or shear and whether the load is parallel to, or perpendicular to, the grain. With the exception that 1 and 2 below are reversed for strength classes SC1, SC2, SC3, and SC4, the grade stresses can be ranked, starting with the strongest, as follows:

1   Bending parallel to the grain.
2   Compression parallel to the grain.
3   Tension parallel to the grain.
4   Compression perpendicular to the grain.
5   Shear parallel to the grain.

Using 1 to 5 above it is possible to decide which is the most effective way of using structural timber.


## 1.6   Timber grade stresses

For the structural use of timber, it is the grade stress of each species and grade which is of prime importance. To increase the flexibility of timber supply, a series of nine strength classes is used for design purposes. Guidance as to which species and grade satisfy the strength require-ments for each class is given in BS 5268: Pt 2, Tables 3 to 8 inclusive. This does not preclude the use of a specific species and grade, which may have the required characteristics. These characteristics may be natural durability, amenability to preservatives, glues and fasteners, etc.

The stress values for individual species and grades are given in BS 5268: Pt 2, Tables 10, 11, 12, 13 and 15. Table 14 gives the section size modification factors for North American timbers.

The dimensions of softwoods are given in BS 4471 and the dimensions of hardwoods in BS 5450. The geometrical properties of timbers with these dimensions are given in Appendix D for softwoods and Appendix E for hardwoods and should be used in designing for the dry exposure condition. For the wet exposure condition, the values in Appendix D and Appendix E are modified by the modification factor $K1$ given in Table 1.3.

All timber used for structural work must be stress graded either by visual inspection or by an approved stress-grading machine operated in accordance with the requirements of BS 4978: 1988, *Specification for softwood grades for structural use.*

The visual grades are designated GS and SS. The machine grades are MGS, MSS, M50 and M75. There are the additional machine grades

## Table 1.3  Wet exposure modification factor *K*1

| Geometrical property | Value of K1 |
|---|---|
| Thickness, width, radius of gyration | 1.02 |
| Cross-sectional area | 1.04 |
| First moment of area, section modulus | 1.06 |
| Second moment of area | 1.08 |

Source: Reproduced with permission from BS 5268: Pt 2

selected to comply with the strength class requirements. The S6, S8, MS6 and MS8 grades of the ECE *Recommended standard for stress grading of coniferous sawn timbers* (1982) may be substituted for GS, SS, MGS and MSS respectively.

Timber grade in accordance with certain of the *National grading rules for dimension lumber* (Canada, NLGA 1979), *National grading rules for softwood dimensional lumber* (NGRDL, 1975), *North American Export Standard for Machine grades and tropical hardwoods of visual grade HS* to BS 5756: 1980, *Tropical hardwoods graded for structural use*, satisfy the BS 5268 requirements and may be used structurally (clause 9).

## 1.7  Use of the strength classes and the stress grades

Structural timber design may be based on either the stresses for the strength classes or on the stresses for the individual species and grades. Table 1.4 gives the grade stresses and moduli of elasticity for the strength classes.

When designing using the strength classes, the strength class used (whether the timber is hardwood or softwood and where the timber is limited by factors other than strength) and the required species must be stated. The combination of species and grade is assigned to a particular strength class if the bending and tension stresses of the species/grade combination are appropriate to the depth for bending or width for tension of 300 mm and are not less than the strength class stresses. There is also the additional requirement that the compression stress parallel to the grain, the shear stress parallel to the grain and the modulus of elasticity are not less than 95 per cent of the strength class value. Certain North American softwoods must not be used in tension (BS 5268: Pt 2, clause 10.1).

The designer should be aware that there may be advantages in using

## Table 1.4 Grade stresses and moduli of elasticity for strength classes

| Strength class | Bending parallel to the grain MPa | Tension parallel to the grain MPa | Compression parallel to the grain MPa | Compression perpendicular to the grain* MPa | MPa | Shear parallel to the grain MPa | Modulus of elasticity Mean MPa | Minimum MPa |
|---|---|---|---|---|---|---|---|---|
| SC1 | 2.8 | 2.2 | 3.5 | 2.1 | 1.2 | 0.46 | 6 800 | 4 500 |
| SC2 | 4.1 | 2.5 | 5.3 | 2.1 | 1.6 | 0.66 | 8 000 | 5 000 |
| SC3 | 5.3 | 3.2 | 6.8 | 2.2 | 1.7 | 0.67 | 8 800 | 5 800 |
| SC4 | 7.5 | 4.5 | 7.9 | 2.4 | 1.9 | 0.71 | 9 900 | 6 600 |
| SC5 | 10.0 | 6.0 | 8.7 | 2.8 | 2.4 | 1.00 | 10 700 | 7 100 |
| SC6 | 12.5 | 7.5 | 12.5 | 3.8 | 2.8 | 1.50 | 14 100 | 11 800 |
| SC7 | 15.0 | 9.0 | 14.5 | 4.4 | 3.3 | 1.75 | 16 200 | 13 600 |
| SC8 | 17.5 | 10.5 | 16.5 | 5.2 | 3.9 | 2.00 | 18 700 | 15 600 |
| SC9 | 20.5 | 12.3 | 19.5 | 6.1 | 4.6 | 2.25 | 21 600 | 18 000 |

*Note: When wane is not allowed at the bearing area, the higher stress values for compression perpendicular to the grain may be used, otherwise the lower values must be used.
Source: Reproduced with permission from BS 5268: Pt 2

the strength class system, rather than an individual species and grade. The converse is also true. Usually, specifying a higher strength class, say specifying SC5 instead of SC3, will increase timber costs and reduce timber availability.

In general, fastener loads are related to the strength class of the timber, but there are exceptions and these are dealt with in Chapter 9 (BS 5268: Pt 2, clause 38).

## 1.8  Additional properties

Unless specific test data is available, the values given in Table 1.5 should be assumed:

### Table 1.5  Additional properties

| Properties required | Fraction of known value for timber |
|---|---|
| (a)  Tension perpendicular to grain<br>Torsional shear<br>Rolling shear | 1/3 of shear parallel to the grain |
| (b)  Modulus of elasticity<br>     perpendicular to the grain | 1/20 of the permissible modulus of elasticity |
| (c)  Shear modulus | 1/16 of the permissible modulus of elasticity |

If the direction of load is inclined at an angle $\alpha$ to the grain, then the permissible compressive stress for the inclined surface is given by:

$$\sigma_{c,\text{adm},\alpha} = \sigma_{c,\text{adm},\|} - (\sigma_{c,\text{adm},\|} - \sigma_{c,\text{adm},\perp}) \times \sin \alpha \tag{1.1}$$

The grade compressive stress parallel to the grain ($\sigma_{c,\,adm,\,\|}$) and the grade compressive stress perpendicular to the grain ($\sigma_{c,\,adm,\,\perp}$) must be modified as appropriate for the moisture content, section size and duration of loading (see Chapter 2 and BS 5268: Pt 2, clauses 10.2 and 12).

## 1.9  Modification factors

BS 5268: Pt 2 lists 87 modification factors to be used in structural timber design. Table 1.6 lists those modification factors and where they are to be used and can be used as a means of checking that the correct modification factors have been considered in a particular structural timber design.

## Table 1.6  Modification factors

| Where modification factor used | Modification factor |
| --- | --- |
| Wet exposure condition | $K1$, $K2$ |
| Duration of load | $K3$, $K71$, $K81$ |
| Flexural members | $K4$, $K5$, $K6$, $K7$, $K8$, $K9$, $K11$ |
| Compression members | $K10$, $K11$, $K12$, $K13$ |
| Tension members | $K14$ |
| Glued laminated members | $K15$, $K16$, $K17$, $K18$, $K19$, $K20$, $K21$, $K22$, $K23$, $K24$, $K25$, $K26$, $K27$, $K28$, $K29$, $K30$, $K31$, $K32$, $K33$, $K34$, $K35$, |
| Plywood | $K36$, $K37$ |
| Tempered hardboard | $K38$, $K39$, $K40$, $K41$, $K71$, $K72$ |
| Nailed connectors | $K43$, $K44$, $K45$, $K46$, $K47$, $K48$, $K49$, $K50$, $K70$ |
| Screwed connectors | $K43$, $K46$, $K51$, $K52$, $K53$, $K54$ |
| Bolted connectors | $K42$, $K46$, $K55$, $K56$, $K57$ |
| Toothed-plate connectors | $K42$, $K58$, $K59$, $K60$, $K61$, $KC$, $KS$ |
| Split-ring connectors | $K42$, $K62$, $K63$, $K64$, $K65$, $KC$, $KD$, $KS$ |
| Shear-plate connectors | $K42$, $K66$, $K67$, $K68$, $K69$, $KC$, $KD$, $KS$ |
| Strength test | $K72$, $K73$, $K80$ |
| Clear wood stresses | $K74$, $K75$, $K76$, $K77$, $K78$ |
| Chipboard | $K79$, $K80$, $K81$, $K82$, $K83$, $K84$ |

## 1.10  Durability

The durability of timber is related to the length of time a piece of heartwood, when in contact with damp soil, would resist fungal attack. In structural timber design, it is preferable that heartwood should be used and not the sapwood, which is less durable.

The classification of timber durability shown in Table 1.7 very much underestimates the service life of structural timber. The designer would

### Table 1.7 Timber durability

| Level of durability | Years in contact with damp soil |
|---|---|
| Very durable | 25 |
| Durable | 15 to 25 |
| Moderately durable | 10 to 15 |
| Non-durable | 5 to 10 |
| Perishable | less than 5 |

ensure that the timber was not in contact with damp soil and that the moisture content was in accordance with Table 1.2. Attention to detailing and the application of preservative chemicals would also increase the service life.


## 1.11  Workmanship

It is assumed that:

1  all materials are able to perform the function for which they are required;
2  workmanship conforms to accepted good practice;
3  there will be adequate preparation and construction supervision;
4  no member exceeds its permitted deflection limit;
5  all members and materials conform to the drawings and specification;
6  all materials are stored undistorted and undercover;
7  during assembly and erection the permissible member stress is not exceeded;
8  damaged members are repaired or replaced to the designer's and approving authorities' satisfaction; and
9  for chipboard all the BS 5669 recommendations should be followed.


## 1.12  Amendments to BS 5268: Pt 2

It is necessary to ensure from the latest BSI Standards catalogue that the copy of BS 5268: Pt 2 being used has all the necessary BS amendments and has not been superseded.

## 1.13 Design example 1: Solid timber compression member and joint

*A solid timber compression member, to be used internally, is to be designed with bolted connectors. Determine the modification factors that need to be considered in the design.*

The modification factors to be considered are found from Table 1.6 and are as follows:

1 Duration of load       – $K3$
2 Compression members – $K10$, $K11$, $K12$, $K13$
3 Bolted connectors      – $K42$, $K46$, $K55$, $K56$, $K57$.

# 2 Loading

## 2.1 Introduction

All timber structures and structural timber members must be capable of carrying their design dead loads, imposed loads, wind loads and all other types of loads specified in BS 5268, safely to the ground. The design loads must not cause excessive deflection or deformation of any structural members and the resulting timber stresses must not exceed those given in BS 5268.

A major advantage of timber as a structural material is that, by reducing the length of time a load is applied to a structural timber element, the greater the load the timber element can resist.

## 2.2 Loading types

The loads on structural timber members are arranged into four load duration categories as shown in Table 2.1. The modification factors $K3$, $K38$ and $K81$ are used to modify the stresses given in BS 5268 which apply to the long-term loading. Where the value of $K3$ exceeds 1.00, it is necessary to check all the loading cases to ensure that the resulting stresses are not exceeded for any other relevant loading condition. With the exception of the modulus of elasticity and the shear modulus, $K3$ is applicable to all the timber properties.

For uniformly distributed imposed floor loads, $K3 = 1.0$ except where

## Table 2.1  Duration of loading

| Load duration | Combination of loads | Value of K3 | Value of K38 | Value of K81 |
|---|---|---|---|---|
| Long term | 1 dead + permanent imposed | 1.00 | 1.00 | 1.00 |
| Medium term | 1 dead + snow | | | |
| | 2 dead + temporary imposed | 1.25 | 1.50 | 1.80 |
| Short term | 1 dead + imposed + wind | | | |
| | 2 dead + imposed + snow + wind | 1.50 | 2.25 | 3.20 |
| Very short term | 1 dead + imposed + wind | 1.75 | 2.50 | 3.50 |

Source: Reproduced with permission from BS 5268: Pt 2

higher loads are specified to cater for occasional crowd loading such as in corridors, hallways and landings when $K3$ may be assumed to be 1.25.

For trussed rafters, additional loadings due to their transportation and handling between manufacture and final positioning have to be considered, but it is assumed that reasonable care will be taken to reduce these loadings.

## 2.3   Duration of load

Long-term loading includes all dead loads, self-weight loads and permanently imposed loads such as partitions, which may be expected to be in place throughout the life of the member or structure.

Medium-term loading includes dead loads and snow loads which may be in place for a number of weeks in combination with temporary imposed loads.

Short-term loads include dead loads, imposed loads and snow loads in combination, together with wind loading of 15-second gusts.

Very short-term loading includes dead load, imposed load and wind load of 3- to 5-second gusts.

For domestic floors, the possible concentrated loading condition given in BS 6399: Pt 1, that is, 1.4 kN, may be superimposed on the dead load and both treated as of medium-term duration.

## 2.4   Dead load

The value of the dead load is found in accordance with BS 6399: Pt 1 and is defined as the load due to the weight of all walls, permanent partitions, floors, roofs and finishes, including services and all other permanent construction. The unit weights may be the actual known weights or those given in BS 648. In the case of tanks and other receptacles, they must be considered when full and when empty.

For trussed rafters where the common type of concrete interlocking tiles are used, it is assumed that the dead load on the rafter member is 0.685 kN/m$^2$ measured along the slope. For other types of rafter covering the actual dead load is used. The dead load on a ceiling tie is assumed to be 0.25 kN/m$^2$ and a concentrated load of 0.45 kN at each of two node points nearest to the tank in each trussed rafter. If there is no tank, the 0.45 kN concentrated loads may be ignored, but account must be taken of other services permanently supported by the trussed rafter.

## 2.5 Imposed load

The value of the imposed load is found using BS 6399: Pt 1 and includes the weights of any movable partitions, concentrated loads, impact loads, inertia loads and snow loads. To assist in determining the required imposed load, there are ten occupancy classes as follows:

1  Residential type 1
2  Residential type 2
3  Residential type 3
4  Institutional and educational
5  Public assembly
6  Offices
7  Retail
8  Industrial
9  Storage
10  Vehicular

### 2.5.1  Imposed floor loads

In BS 6399: Pt 1, each occupancy class is illustrated with examples of typical structures. A value of distributed load and concentrated load is given for each floor area usage. For some floor usages, the distributed load is adequate and no concentrated load value is given.

The distributed load and the concentrated load must be checked individually to determine the maximum stress and maximum deflection. The concentrated load may need to be placed in a number of positions to obtain these maximum values. For shear and bending calculations, the concentrated load is assumed to act at a point, but for crushing, punching and other local effects, the actual area of load application is used. If the floor is capable of effective lateral distribution the concentrated load need not be considered.

If partitions are not positioned at the design stage but are to be added at a later date, it is usual to add a UDL per square metre of one-third of the finished partition weight per metre run but with a minimum value of $1.0 \text{ kN/m}^2$. For beams, the imposed load is the distributed load.

With the exception of any plant or machinery which has been specifically allowed for, or for buildings for storage purposes, garages and warehouses, the imposed floor loads may, in certain circumstances, be reduced. When designing columns, piers, walls, beams, their supports and foundations, the reductions shown in Tables 2.2 and 2.3 can be used. If the floor is designed to carry $5 \text{ kN/m}^2$ or more, then the reductions shown in Table 2.2 can still be used, provided the reduced loading does not fall below $5 \text{ kN/m}^2$, in which case $5 \text{ kN/m}^2$ will be used. The reductions shown in Table 2.3 do not apply to roofs.

**Table 2.2   Reduction in total distributed imposed floor loads with number of storeys**

| Number of floors, including roof, carried by the member under construction | Reduction in total distributed imposed load on all floors carried by the member under consideration (%) |
|---|---|
| 1 | 0 |
| 2 | 10 |
| 3 | 20 |
| 4 | 30 |
| 5 to 10 | 40 |
| over 10 | 50 |

For single span beams or girders, there is an alternative reduction in imposed load, as given in Table 2.3, provided the area supported by the beam or girder is not less than $40 \text{ m}^2$ at the same general level.

The maximum reduction is 25 per cent and may be used when designing the columns supporting such a beam. The reductions given in Table 2.2 or those given in Table 2.3 may be used, whichever is the greater.

## 2.5.2   Flat roofs

Roofs between $0°$ and $10°$ to the horizontal are considered as flat roofs and are divided into two groups. The first group are roofs where there is

**Table 2.3  Reduction in total distributed imposed floor loads on a supporting beam or girder with floor area**

| Area supported (m²) | Reduction in total distributed imposed load (%) |
|---|---|
| ⩽ 40 | 0 |
| 80 | 5 |
| 120 | 10 |
| 160 | 15 |
| 200 | 20 |
| ⩾ 240 | 25 maximum |

no access, except for cleaning and repair. The second group are roofs where access is allowed in addition to cleaning and repairs. In the former, the imposed distributed load, including snow load is $0.75 \text{ kN/m}^2$, measured on the plan, or a 0.9 kN concentrated load. In the latter, the loads are doubled to $1.5 \text{ kN/m}^2$ and 1.8 kN, respectively. The load which gives the maximum stress or the maximum deflection is used. The loads are assumed to act vertically.

### 2.5.3  Sloping roofs

For roofs with a pitch from 10° to 30°, it is assumed that there is no access other than for cleaning and maintenance, and the imposed distributed load and concentrated load are the same as for a flat roof with the same access, namely $0.75 \text{ kN/m}^2$ and 0.9 kN. For roof pitches greater than 30°, the imposed distributed load is $0.75 \text{ kN/m}^2$, and $0.0 \text{ kN/m}^2$ at 75° pitch. Linear interpolation of the load is used for pitches between 30° and 75°. The 0.9 kN concentrated load is not reduced, but it is usually the less severe load.

### 2.5.4  Curved roofs

For curved roofs, the imposed load is calculated by dividing the roof into at least five equal segments and calculating the load on each segment using its mean slope.

### 2.5.5  Roof covering

With the exception of glazing, all self-supporting roof coverings, with a slope of less than 45°, must be able to support a 0.9 kN load, incidental to maintenance, concentrated over a 125 mm square.

## 2.5.6 Ceiling ties

The imposed load on a ceiling tie is a $0.25$ kN/m$^2$ UDL over the whole ceiling area plus a $0.9$ kN concentrated load placed to give the maximum stress. If no access is provided to the roof space, both the UDL and the concentrated load can be ignored.

## 2.5.7 Snow loads

The snow load on a roof is included in the imposed roof load, but its value may be increased locally if higher snow loads are expected due to wind, the roof slope, or the snow sliding, drifting or melting.

The effect of exceptional loads caused by 'local drifting of snow' on roofs as defined in BS 6399: Pt 3 should be checked, on the assumption that such loads are accidental.

# 2.6 Wind loading

Wind loads are calculated using CP3, Chapter V, Part 2. From the consideration of the basic wind speed $V$, applicable to the area where the structure is to be built, a design wind speed $V_s$ is found by modifying $V$, using three modification factors $S_1$, $S_2$ and $S_3$. $S_1$ is a topography factor, which takes into account the ground surface variations. The second factor, $S_2$, the ground roughness factor, relates the structure cladding (Class A) and structure size (Class B or C) to the building position in relation to other wind obstructions. The third modification factor, $S_3$, is a statistical factor that takes into account the degree of structural security required. Using the design wind speed $V_s$, the dynamic wind pressure, $q$, is obtained.

Wind can produce both suction and pressure on a structure and $q$ is modified by both an internal pressure coefficient $C_{pi}$ and an external pressure coefficient $C_{pe}$. The load on the surface of a structure is $q$ times the algebraic sum of $C_{pi}$ and $C_{pe}$ multiplied by the area of wind loading.

For trussed rafter roofs, CP3, Chapter V, Part 2 is modified by ignoring the greatest horizontal and vertical dimensions of the roof and designing it as a Class B structure.

Wind loading is a complex form of loading, but for timber structures, which are lightweight structures, wind uplift can be particularly important when considering overall structural stability. Positive fixings are required between the roof and the walls to prevent the roof lifting off and between the walls and the foundation to prevent the whole building lifting off.

## 2.7 Load combinations

In assessing which loads are considered to be long term, medium term, short term or very short term, both Parts 2 and 3 of BS 5268 must be used. In Part 2, the load combinations suggested are given in Table 2.1 but are modified in two ways. Firstly, the imposed floor load is considered as a long-term load and, secondly, the wind loading can be either a short-term loading, if the structure is Class C, or a very short-term load for structures in Class A or B. For domestic floors the concentrated loading of 1.4 kN can also be superimposed on the dead load and both treated as a medium-term load.

For trussed rafter roofs, Part 3 gives the load type combinations to be considered related to the different load durations. Tables 2.4 and 2.5 give the summary of rafter and ceiling tie loads, respectively, and Table 2.6, the load combinations.

### Table 2.4 Summary of rafter loads

| Type | Load | Position on rafter | Duration |
|---|---|---|---|
| 1 Dead | (a) 0.685 kN/m² UDL (measured along the slope), or (b) actual known loads | Full length | Long term |
| 2 Imposed | (a) Pitch 10° to 30° UDL 0.75 kN/m² (measured on plan), or | Full length | Medium term |
| | (b) 0.9 kN concentrated load | Centre of any bay | Short term |
| 3 | (a) Pitch more than 30° UDL varying from 0.75 kN/m² at 30° to 0.0 kN/m² at 75° (measured on plan) | Full length | Medium term |
| 4 Wind | (a) Wind calculated according to CP3, Chapter V, Part 2 for Class B structures | Full length | Very short term |

Note: Load type 3 is assumed to act at the centre of the rafter bay in which it produces the most adverse effect.

### Table 2.5  Summary of ceiling tie loads

| Type | Load | Position on ceiling tie | Duration |
|---|---|---|---|
| 5 *Dead* | (a) 0.25 kN/m² UDL | Full length | Long term |
| | plus 2 × 0.45 kN | At 2 nodes | Long term |
| | concentrated loads | nearest water | |
| | for water tanks or | tank | |
| | actual load if greater | | Long term |
| | plus plant and special | | Long term |
| | services | As appropriate | |
| 6 *Imposed* | 0.25 kN/m² UDL | Full length | Long term |
| 7 *Imposed* | 0.9 kN concentrated load | Centre or either end of any bay | Short term |

Note: Load type 7 is assumed to act at either the centre of the ceiling tie bay or at a node point, whichever produces the most adverse effect. It is assumed that between 75 and 100 per cent of the concentrated load is carried by the appropriate ceiling tie and that the remainder is transferred to the neighbouring trussed rafters through the attached ceiling tie boarding.

### Table 2.6  Rafter and ceiling tie load combinations

| Load duration | | Load combination |
|---|---|---|
| (a) | Long term | 1 + 5 + 6 |
| (b) | Medium term | 1 + 2 + 5 + 6 |
| (c) | Short term | 1 + 2 + 5 + 6 + 7 |
| (d) | Short term | 1 + 3 + 5 + 6 |
| (e) | Very short term | 1 + 4 + 5 |
| (f) | Very short term | 1 + 4 + 5 + 6 + 7 |
| (g) | Very short term | 1 + 2 + 4 + 5 + 6 + 7 |

## 2.8  Load-sharing systems

If four or more structural members, such as rafters, joists, beams, trusses or wall studs are:

(a)   spaced at a maximum of 610 mm centre to centre,
(b)   adequately laterally connected, and
(c)   form a load-sharing system,

then the appropriate grade stresses are multiplied by the load-sharing modification factor $K8$ which has a value of 1.1.

The load-sharing system also allows the mean modulus of elasticity to be used to determine displacements and deflections under both dead and imposed loading. If the imposed loading is due to mechanical plant or equipment, or for floors subjected to vibration, the minimum modulus of elasticity must be used.

The load-sharing modification factor does not apply to the calculation of the modification factor $K8$ for load-sharing columns, nor does it apply to the bending stresses in ceiling ties, unless the ceiling ties have binders or boarding other than plaster boarding to ensure adequate load distribution.

If two or more trussed rafters are permanently fastened directly together and used as principal members, the grade stresses and minimum modulus of elasticity can be altered by using the load-sharing modification factors shown in Table 2.7 (Table 10 in BS 5268: Pt 3).

**Table 2.7   Load-sharing factors for principal trussed rafters**

| Number of units | Load-sharing factor | |
| --- | --- | --- |
| | For stresses | For modulus of elasticity |
| 1 | 1.0 | 1.00 |
| 2 | 1.1 | 1.14 |
| 3 | 1.1 | 1.21 |
| 4 or more | 1.1 | 1.24 |

## 2.9   Accidental loading

In the design of structures and structural members, the loading due to normal expected use is quantified, but there is a duty to design in such a way that any misuse or accident does not cause catastrophic collapse. Damage should be in proportion to its cause. To this end designers should consider some sort of protection to structural members, for example vehicle crash barriers around structural columns. For residual stability loading calculations, designers should consider an assumed mode of damage but they can multiply by two the long-term permissible stresses and the permissible loads on the fasteners.

For structures up to four storeys, there are no specific additional design requirements for accidental damage, but for over four storeys, where timber is a minor load-bearing material used in conjunction with other load-bearing materials, the relevant accidental loadings specified in the other materials standard should be used.

The effect of exceptional loads caused by 'local drifting of snow' on roofs as defined in BS 6399: Pt 3 should be checked, on the assumption that such loads are accidental.

## 2.10   Handling loads

For trussed rafters, a handling force of 1.5 kN in any direction in its plane must be included in the design, but for other timber members, care must be exercised in their handling and the designer will suggest a method of handling and mark lifting points.

## 2.11   Load testing

It is usual to design structures fabricated from timber and/or plywood, and partly or wholly from tempered hardboard or wholly from chipboard by calculation, but load testing is an equally acceptable alternative. The load testing uses the dead load and the design load, which is a reasonable combination of dead, imposed and wind loading that gives the worst loading condition for the test.

The dead loading is used for the pre-load test and the design load for the deflection test. Two and a half times the design load is used in the strength test for timber and/or plywood structures. In the strength test for partly or wholly tempered hardboard structures the maximum load is the modification factor $K71$ times the design load, where $K71$ has the values shown in Table 2.8 (Table 89). If the tempered hardboard is acting compositely with timber, the maximum load for the strength test is the sum of 2.5 times the share of the design load carried by the timber and $K71$ times the share of the design load carried by the tempered hardboard. The stiffness properties of the composite section for the purpose of estimating the load apportionment are calculated and for tempered hardboard the moduli are taken into account using a value of 4.20 for $K39$, $K40$ and $K41$.

In the strength test for partly or wholly chipboard structures, the maximum load is the design load times the modification factor $K79$, where $K79$ has the value shown in Table 2.8 (Table 89a). If the chipboard is acting compositely with the timber, the maximum load for the strength test is the sum of 2.5 times the share of the design load carried by the timber and $K79$ times the share of the design load carried by the chipboard. In calculating the stiffness properties of the composite

**21**

**Table 2.8  Modification factors $K71$ and $K79$ for the strength test of tempered hardboard structures and chipboard structures**

| Load duration | Value of K71 | Value of K79 |
|---|---|---|
| Long term | 5.3 | 3.41 |
| Medium term | 3.6 | 1.85 |
| Short term | 2.3 | 1.06 |
| Very short term | 2.2 | 0.96 |

Source: Reproduced with permission from BS 5268: Pt 2

section for the purpose of estimating the load apportionment, the moduli of the chipboard are taken into account using $K82 = K83 = K84 = 5.24$.

If the tempered hardboard and timber are not acting compositely, the load is $K71$ times the design load in the tempered hardboard and 2.5 times the design load in the timber. Due to the different load factors for the two materials, it may be necessary to strength test the timber and tempered hardboard of an additional component separately.

If the chipboard and the timber are not acting compositely, the load is $K79$ times the design load in the chipboard parts and 2.5 times the design load in the timber parts. Due to the different load factors for the two materials, it may be necessary to separately strength test the timber parts and chipboard parts of an additional component.

For domestic floors, the 1.4 kN concentrated load may be superimposed on the dead load and both treated as a medium-term load. For trussed rafters, the dead load applied during the pre-load test consists of the dead load types 1 and 5 of Tables 2.4 and 2.5. The design load used for the deflection tests consists of load types 1, 2, 5, 6 and 7 of Tables 2.4 and 2.5, or another more appropriate or onerous load combination. The position of the type 7 concentrated load must be agreed for its use in the first part of the deflection test. It is not used in the second part of the test. In the strength test, the design load types 1, 2, 5 and 6 are increased to 2.5 times their value, but load type 7 is not increased.

## 2.12  Other types of loading

There are other types of loading to which a timber structure may be subjected; for example the internal pressure on timber containers, dynamic loading on crane gantry girders, parapets, balustrades and vehicle barriers. These are not the usual forms of loading on timber structures or specified in BS 5268, and in these cases, reference must be made to BS 6399: Pt 1 for guidance.

## 2.13 Future British Standards on loading

One further part of BS 6399 is being prepared; it is Part 2, *Code of practice on wind loads* which will replace CP3, Chapter V, Part 2.

## 2.14 Design example 1: The loading on a timber floor joist

*Determine the long-term load and medium-term load carried by a timber joisted floor, where the joists are spaced at 750 mm centres and have an effective span of 5 metres. The joist self dead load including the sheet material flooring and ceiling covering is 0.4 kN/m². The occupancy class is residential type 1.*

1  *Long-term loading*
The long-term loading comprises dead and permanently imposed load as shown in (a) and (b).

(a)  Dead load: $0.4 \text{ kN/m}^2 \times 5$ m span $\times 0.750$ m
     centres                                                    = 1.5 kN UDL
(b)  Permanently imposed load: where the
     positions of the partitions are not shown, a
     load of $1 \text{ kN/m}^2$ is assumed.
     $1.0 \text{ kN/m}^2 \times 5$ m span $\times 0.750$ m centres        = 3.75 kN UDL
                                                    Total     5.25 kN UDL

2  *Medium-term loading*
The medium-term loading is the dead load plus the temporary imposed distributed load or temporary imposed concentrated load as shown in (a), (b) and (c) below.

(a)  Dead load: As found in (a) and (b) above    =  5.25 kN UDL
(b) and (c)                                       _____
Temporary imposed:
  (b)  $1.5 \text{ kN/m}^2 \times 5$ m span $\times 0.750$ m centres    =  5.63 kN UDL
  (c)  1.4 kN concentrated load                   =  1.4 kN
                      Total (a) + (b)             = 10.88 kN UDL
                      (a) + (c) = 5.25 kN UDL + 1.4 kN

The medium-term load is a combination of a UDL and a concentrated load and can be dealt with in three ways. Firstly, the calculation can take into account the UDL and concentrated loads separately and, because the BS assumes a linearly elastic analysis, the principle of superposition can be applied. Secondly, if the floor has the means of effective lateral distribution of the concentrated load, for example by having tongued and grooved boarding or sheet material such as plywood or chipboard, the concentrated load need not be considered. Thirdly, the concentrated load of 1.4 kN will produce the same bending stress as a distributed load of 2 times 1.4 kN or 2.8 kN UDL and will have the same effect on the deflection as a distributed load of 1.6 times 1.4 kN or 2.24 kN UDL.

The joisted floor is assumed to have effective means of lateral support and the concentrated load can be eliminated. The loading to be considered is as follows:

(a)  Long-term loading     =  5.25 kN UDL
(b)  Medium-term loading  = 10.88 kN UDL

In order to determine which loading is likely to produce the greatest stress, the loading is divided by the appropriate stress modification factor $K3$ of Table 2.1 as follows:

(a)  Long-term loading     =  5.25 kN ÷ 1.0  = 5.25 kN UDL
(b)  Medium-term loading  = 10.88 kN ÷ 1.25 = 8.70 kN UDL

The medium-term loading is the largest and is the critical loading condition, but both the long-term and medium-term loading could be reduced if the positions of the partitions are specified and joists positioned under them. For some small span beams, the dead load plus the concentrated load may be the critical loading.

## 2.15   Design example 2: The loading on a trussed rafter

*Determine the long-term, medium-term, short-term and very short-term loads on a trussed rafter of 12 m span, 20° roof pitch and spaced at 600 mm centres.*

The rafter loads, ceiling tie loads and load combinations are those specified in Tables 2.4, 2.5 and 2.6 (7 and 8 of BS 5268: Pt 3).

(a)  *Summary of rafter loads*

Type 1   0.685 kN/m² (12 × (1/cos 20°))
           roof pitch × 0.600 m spacing                = 5.25 kN UDL

Type 2   0.75 kN/m² × 12 m span × 0.600 m spacing   = 5.40 kN UDL
Type 3   0.9 kN concentrated load                           = 0.9 kN
Type 4   Wind load. Calculated for a roof as appropriate for a Class
         B structure according to CP3, Chapter V, Part 2 as follows:

The dynamic pressure $q$, is given by $q = 0.613\ V_s^2$ N/m²

where $V$ = the basic wind speed, here taken as 44 m/s, $S_1$ = topography factor and taken as 1.0, $S_2$ = ground roughness and here taken as 0.74, and, $S_3$ = statistical factor and taken as 1.0.
   Using $V_s = V \times S_1 \times S_2 \times S_3$ gives the following value for $q$:

$q = 0.613 \times (44\text{ m/s} \times 1 \times 0.74 \times 1)^2$ N/m²
$\quad = 0.650$ kN/m²

The wind forces on the roof are found using the internal pressure coefficients $C_{pi}$ and the external pressure coefficients $C_{pe}$ as follows:

$$F = (C_{pe} - C_{pi})\ q\ A$$

where $A$ = area in m².
   There are two wind load conditions to be considered; firstly, the maximum wind uplift on the roof and, secondly, the maximum downward wind load, both measured along the slope. The values of the coefficients are shown in Figure 2.1.
   Maximum uplift on the roof per trussed rafter:

$F = (-0.8 - 0.2) \times 0.650$ kN/m² $\times$
$(12 \times \left(\dfrac{1}{\cos 20°}\right) \times 0.600$ m) spacing
$= -4.98$ kN UDL uplift

Maximum downward load on the roof per trussed rafter:

$F = (-0.5 + 0.3) \times 0.650$ kN/m² $\times$
$(12 \times \left(\dfrac{1}{\cos 20°}\right) \times 0.600$ m) spacing
$= -1.00$ kN UDL uplift

giving type 4 wind load values of either $-4.98$ kN UDL or $-1.00$ kN UDL.
   In this example it has been assumed that the value of $C_{pe}$ is the same on both sides of the roof slope, but it is possible to have different values which, when they occur, must be used.

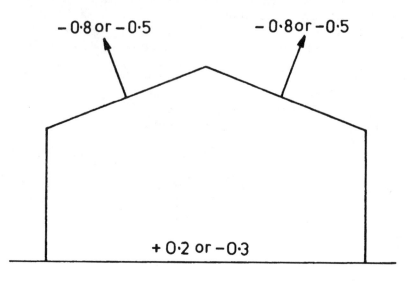

**Figure 2.1   Wind coefficients $C_{pe}$ and $C_{pi}$**
$C_{pe}$ = either −0.8 or −0.5, $C_{pi}$ = either +0.2 or −0.3

(b)   *Summary of ceiling tie loads*

| | | | |
|---|---|---|---|
| Type 5 | I | 0.25 kN/m² × 12 m span × 0.600 m spacing | = 1.8 kN UDL |
| | II | plus 2 × 0.45 kN concentrated loads | = 2 × 0.45 kN |
| | III | plus plant and special services | = 0.0 kN |
| Type 6 | | 0.25 kN/m² × 12 m span × 0.600 m spacing | = 1.8 kN UDL |
| Type 7 | | 0.9 kN concentrated load | = 0.9 kN |

Bringing together the load combinations given in Table 2.6 and subsituting the values of the load types 1 to 7 into Table 2.6, the values of the load combinations are as given in Table 2.9.

From Table 2.9, it is not immediately obvious which loading condition is likely to be critical, but by carrying out two operations a guide to the most likely critical loading condition may be found. The first operation is to change the concentrated loads into an equivalent UDL, by adding together the concentrated load for the load combination under consideration and multiply it by two to determine a UDL which will produce the same bending stress as the concentrated load. The second operation is to divide the UDL by the value of $K3$ given in Table 2.1. The largest value of UDL is then the most likely to be the

**Table 2.9   Value of the load combinations**

| Duration of loading | Combination | Rafter load | Ceiling tie load |
|---|---|---|---|
| (a) Long term | 1 + 5 + 6 | 5.25 kN UDL + | { 3.6 kN UDL |
| (b) Medium term | 1 + 5 + 6 + 2 | 10.65 kN UDL + | { 2 × 0.45 kN |
| (c) Short term | 1 + 5 + 6 + 2 + 7 | 10.65 kN UDL + | { 3.6 kN UDL<br>{ 2 × 0.45 kN<br>{ 0.9 kN |
| (d) Short term | 1 + 5 + 6 + 3 | 5.25 kN UDL<br>0.9 kN UDL } + | { 3.6 kN UDL<br>{ 2 × 0.45 kN |
| (e) Very short term | 1 + 5 + 4 | 0.270 kN UDL or<br>4.25 kN UDL } + | { 1.8 kN UDL<br>{ 2 × 0.45 kN |
| (f) Very short term | 1 + 5 + 6 + 7 + 4 | 0.270 kN UDL or<br>4.25 kN UDL } + | { 3.6 kN UDL<br>{ 0.9 kN<br>{ 2 × 0.45 kN |
| (g) Very short term | 1 + 5 + 6 + 7 +<br>4 + 2 | 5.670 kN UDL or<br>9.65 kN UDL } + | { 3.6 kN UDL<br>{ 0.9 kN<br>{ 2 × 0.45 kN |

critical loading. The two operations have been carried out and are shown in Table 2.10.

**Table 2.10   Converted load combinations**

| Duration of loading | Value of K3 | Value of the converted loading Rafter loading | Ceiling tie loading |
|---|---|---|---|
| (a) Long term | 1.0 | 5.25 kN UDL | 5.45 kN UDL |
| (b) Medium term | 1.25 | 8.52 kN UDL | 4.32 kN UDL |
| (c) Short term | 1.5 | 7.10 kN UDL | 4.8 kN UDL |
| (d) Short term | 1.5 | 4.70 kN UDL | 3.6 kN UDL |
| (e) Very short term | 1.75<br>1.75 | 0.15 kN UDL   or<br>2.43 kN UDL | 2.06 kN UDL<br>2.06 kN UDL |
| (f) Very short term | 1.75 | 0.15 kN UDL   or<br>2.43 kN UDL | 4.11 kN UDL<br>4.11 kN UDL |
| (g) Very short term | 1.75 | 3.24 kN UDL   or<br>5.51 kN UDL | 4.11 kN UDL<br>4.11 kN UDL |

From Table 2.10, the largest value of the rafter load is the medium-term loading (b) and the short-term loading (c). For the ceiling tie loading the largest value is the long-term loading (a) and the short-term loading (c). It is likely that the critical loading condition would be (a), (b) or (c) of Table 2.6.

With respect to wind loading, it is necessary to consider both the maximum uplift and the minimum uplift as it is possible for the maximum uplift to exceed the dead load and lift off the roof tiles.

## 2.16   Conclusion

The determination of the most critical load combinations is a significant part of timber design calculations, but experience will often suggest which load combination to check first. Usually the medium-term loading is critical and should be checked first.

# 3 Flexural members; the bending of beams

## 3.1 Introduction

The permissible stresses for flexural members are found from the grade stresses for the strength class and individual species of BS 5268: Pt 2, clause 10, modified by the appropriate modification factor. The permissible stresses depend upon the exposure condition, the duration of loading, load sharing, length and position of bearing, the effective span, the shear at the notched ends, the form factor, the depth factor and the amount of lateral support. Consideration must also be given to such items as notched beams, built-up beams, trimmer joists, lintel, horizontally and vertically glued laminated members, plywood flexural members and tempered hardboard flexural members.

## 3.2 Exposure condition

The dry grade stresses for strength classes (Table 1.4), individual softwoods (BS 5268: Pt 2, Tables 10, 11, 12 and 13) and hardwood (Table 15) species assume the equilibrium moisture content of the solid timber will not exceed 18 per cent for any significant period. If this is not the case, or the solid timber is more than 100 mm thick, the wet stresses and moduli should be modified using $K2$ (see Table 5.2).

## 3.3   Duration of loading

The dry grade stresses (BS 5268: Pt 2, Tables 9, 10, 11, 12 and 15) are for long-term loading and must be modified using the modification factor $K3$ of Table 2.1 for other load durations.

## 3.4   Load-sharing systems

If four or more members act as a load-sharing system as described in section 2.8, the appropriate grade stresses are multiplied by the load-sharing modification factor $K8$, which has a value of 1.1. The mean modulus of elasticity may be used to calculate deflections and displacements under both dead and imposed loads.

## 3.5   Length and position of bearing

The length and position of the bearing on the side grain of the timber can alter the permissible stress in compression perpendicular to the grain. For bearings of any length at the ends of the member or for bearings 150 mm or more in length in any position on the side grain of the member, the grade stresses for compression perpendicular to the grain are applicable. If the bearing is located at 75 mm or more from the end of the member and is less than 150 mm long, as shown in Figure 3.1, the grade stresses are multiplied by the modification factor $K4$ as shown in Table 3.1.

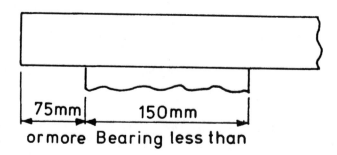

75mm    150mm
or more  Bearing less than

**Figure 3.1   Position of end bearing**
Source:   Reproduced with permission from BS 5268: Pt 2

### Table 3.1 Modification factor *K4* for bearing stress

| Bearing length (mm) | 10 | 15 | 25 | 40 | 50 | 75 | 100 | 150 or more |
|---|---|---|---|---|---|---|---|---|
| Value of $K4$ | | 1.74 | 1.67 | 1.53 | 1.33 | 1.20 | 1.14 | 1.10 | 1.00 |

Source: Reproduced with permission from BS 5268: Pt 2

For bearing lengths between 10 and 150 mm, the value of $K4$ may be interpolated. It is also assumed that the intensity of bearing stress is constant over the bearing area.

## 3.6   Effective span

The effective span is taken as the distance between the centres of the bearings. Often, it will be found that the applied stress in compression perpendicular to the grain is less than the allowable stress in compression perpendicular to the grain and the bearing length could be reduced. If the bearing length is reduced the effective span may also be altered and attention must be paid to the eccentricity of the load on the supporting structure.

## 3.7   Shear at a notched end

Due to the stress concentration that is caused by any sudden change of section in a flexural member, it is not usual to have square-cornered notches at the ends of members. If it is necessary to have notched beams, as shown in Figure 3.2(a) and (b), the maximum permissible shear stress is found from the grade shear stress parallel to the grain multiplied by the modification factor $K5$, with the shear strength being calculated using the effective depth, $h_e$.

If the notch is on the top edge as shown in Figure 3.2(a), then

$$K5 = 1.0 \text{ if } a > h_e$$

and

$$K5 = \frac{h(h_e - a) + ah_e}{h_e^2} \text{ if } a \leqslant h_e$$

If the notch is on the underside, as shown in Figure 3.2(b), then

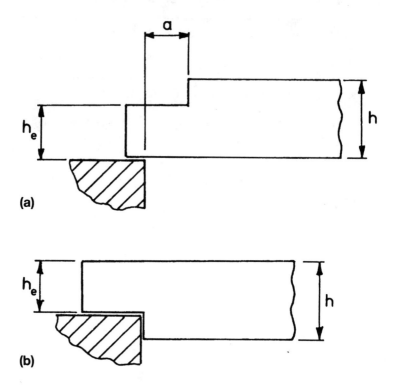

**Figure 3.2 (a) Beam with a notch on the top edge; (b) Beam with a notch on the underside**

Source: Reproduced with permission from BS 5268: Pt 2

$$K5 = \frac{h_e}{h}.$$

The total depth of the beam is $h$, as is shown in Figure 3.2(a). The effective depth $h_e$ should not be less than 0.5 $h$.

## 3.8 Form factor

For flexural members, it is usual to use rectangular sections with two vertical sides and two horizontal sides. If a square section is used and loaded on a diagonal, or a solid circular section is loaded in bending, the modification factor $K6$, with values of 1.41 and 1.18 respectively, is used to multiply the grade bending stresses.

## 3.9 Depth factor

The grade bending stresses given in BS 5268: Pt 2, Tables 9, 10 and 15 are for solid timber with a depth, $h$, of 300 mm and for all thicknesses of laminations graded in accordance with BS 4978 or BS 5756. The reason for specifying a grade bending stress at a specified depth of timber is that the modulus of rupture increases as the timber depth reduces. The grade bending stresses given in BS 5268: Pt 2, Tables 11, 12 and 13 are for solid timber graded to the NLGA or NGRDL joist and plank rules, having a depth $h$ of 300 mm and to the North American MSR rules, having the particular depth quoted; but if graded to the NLGA or NGRDL structural light framing, light framing or stud rules, then the depth $h$ is 89 mm.

For other depths of beams in BS 5268: Pt 2, Tables 9, 10 and 15 and timber graded to NLGA and NGRDL joist and plank rules, the grade bending stresses must be multiplied by the depth modification factor $K7$ as follows:

1  For solid timber beams of depth 72 mm or less, $K7 = 1.17$.
2  If the solid timber beam or glued laminated beam has a depth greater than 72 mm and less than 300 mm, $K7 = (300/h)^{0.11}$.
3  If the solid timber beam or glued laminated beam has a depth greater than 300 mm then

$$K7 = 0.81 \left[\frac{h^2 + 92\,300}{h^2 + 56\,800}\right].$$

For other depths of solid timber graded to North American structural light framing, light framing and stud rules and not assigned to a strength class, the $K7$ modification factor appropriate to their cross-sectional sizes is as given in BS 5268: Pt 2, Table 14. For North American grades not listed in Table 14 and for structural light framing, light framing and stud, 38 mm × 89 mm and all joist and plank grades and sizes, $K11 = 1.0$.

## 3.10 Deflection and stiffness

The dimensions of a flexural member should be such that, when fully loaded, the total deflection does not exceed 0.003 times the span. The total deflection is calculated using the deflection due to bending and the deflection due to shear. In the case of longer span domestic floor joists there is a further restriction that the deflections under the design load do not exceed 14 mm. These deflection limits are required to reduce the possibility of damage to surface materials, ceilings, partitions and finishings as well as to avoid undue vibration.

The deflection under full dead or permanent load may be accounted for by pre-cambering the member and applying the allowable deflection of 0.003 times the span used for the live or intermittent load deflections. If the solid timber member is acting alone, the deflections are calculated using the appropriate minimum modulus of elasticity. The deflections of load-sharing systems, built-up beams and trimmer joists and lintels are calculated as described in sections 2.8, 3.13 and 3.14, respectively.

## 3.11  Lateral support

To ensure that a solid timber or laminated beam of rectangular cross-section does not buckle under its design load, maximum ratios of depth to breadth are specified as shown in Table 3.2. The table may be used as an alternative to the usual methods of calculation.

### Table 3.2  Maximum depth to breadth ratios

| Degree of lateral support | Depth to breadth ratios |
|---|---|
| 1  No lateral support. | 2 |
| 2  Ends held in position. | 3 |
| 3  Ends held in position and members held in line, as by purlins and tie-rods at centres not more than 30 times the breadth of their members. | 4 |
| 4  Ends held in position and compression edge held in line, as by direct connection of sheathing, deck or joists. | 5 |
| 5  Ends held in position and compression edge held in line, as by direct connection of sheathing, deck or joists, together with adequate bridging or blocking spaced at intervals not exceeding six times the depth. | 6 |
| 6  Ends held in position and both edges held firmly in line. | 7 |

Source: Reproduced with permission from BS 5268: Pt 2

## 3.12   Notched beams

If a beam has a notch or a hole through its width, then the effective depth of the beam is reduced by the depth of the notch or the hole and the resulting effective depth is used in the calculations.

For simply-supported floor beams and roof joists, not more than 250 mm deep, the effects of the notches and holes may be ignored, provided either the notches do not exceed 12.5 per cent of the joist depth and are located between 7 and 25 per cent of the span from the support, or the holes are drilled at the neutral axis with diameters not exceeding 25 per cent of the joist depth, with the centres not less than three diameters apart and located between 25 and 40 per cent of the span from the support.

## 3.13   Built-up beams

For built-up beams, it is necessary to consider the possibility of buckling under the design load, especially the concentrated load. For built-up members with thin webs, web stiffeners will be required to provide adequate strength and stability.

The lateral stability of built-up beams can be determined in one of the three following ways:

1   by calculation,
2   by treating the compression flange as a column which may deflect sideways between points of lateral support, and
3   by satisfying the conditions of Table 3.3.

The bending, tension and shear parallel to the grain, the modulus of elasticity and compression parallel to the grain, and the compression perpendicular to the grain for the flanges of glued built-up beams, such as box-beams and I-beams, may be altered by using the respective modification factors $K27$, $K28$ and $K29$ of BS 5268: Pt 2, Table 26. The number of laminations is taken as the number of pieces of timber in each flange, irrespective of their orientation.

For the deflection calculations, where the minimum modulus of elasticity is multiplied by $K28$, the number of laminations to determine the value of $K28$ is the sum of the total number of pieces of timber in both flanges.

For the deflection calculations, both bending deflection and shear deflection must be included.

**35**

## Table 3.3   Lateral stability of built-up beams

| Ratio of the second moment of area of the cross section about the neutral axis to the second moment of area about the axis perpendicular to the neutral axis | Support requirements |
|---|---|
| $\leqslant 5$ to 1 | No lateral support required. |
| between 5 to 1 and 10 to 1 | The ends of the beam must be held in position at the bottom flange at the support. |
| between 10 to 1 and 20 to 1 | The beam must be held in line at the ends. |
| between 20 to 1 and 30 to 1 | One edge must be held in line. |
| between 30 to 1 and 40 to 1 | The beam must be restrained by bridging or other bracing at intervals of not more than 2.4 m. |
| greater than 40 to 1 | The compression flanges should be fully restrained. |

## 3.14   Trimmer joists and lintels

Where two or more joists or lintels are joined together in parallel and act together to support the applied load, the grade stresses in bending and shear parallel to the grain and in compression perpendicular to the grain are multiplied by the load-sharing modification factor $K8$, where $K8 = 1.1$.

When calculating the deflection, the minimum modulus of elasticity is multiplied by $K9$ as given in Table 3.4.

## 3.15   Glued laminated flexural members

Glued laminated flexural members are divided into two sections, those glue laminated vertically and those glue laminated horizontally.

The term 'vertically glued' means a member whose laminations are at right angles to the neutral plane, and the term 'horizontally glued' means a member whose laminations are parallel to the neutral axis.

**Table 3.4  Modification factor K9**

| | Value of K9 | |
| Number of pieces | Softwoods | Hardwoods |
|---|---|---|
| 1 | 1.00 | 1.00 |
| 2 | 1.14 | 1.06 |
| 3 | 1.21 | 1.08 |
| 4 or more | 1.24 | 1.10 |

Source: Reproduced with permission from BS 5268: Pt 2

Vertically-glued laminated beams are subject to the exposure conditions (section 3.2), duration of loading (section 3.3), and the load-sharing systems (section 3.4) requirements when determining the permissible stresses. In addition, the modification factors $K27$ for bending, tension and shear parallel to the grain, $K28$ for modulus of elasticity and compression parallel to the grain and $K29$ for compression perpendicular to the grain given in BS 5268: Pt 2, Table 26 must be used appropriate to the number of laminations. (The modification factors of Table 26 do not apply to the laminating grades but to the softwood and hardwood graded to the structural timber grades.)

The permissible stresses for glued laminated timber flexural members which are horizontally laminated are subject to the requirements of this chapter with the exception that Table 24 and the modification factors $K27$, $K28$ and $K29$ do not apply, but the additional factors given in Chapter 6 must be considered.

Both shear deflection and bending deflection must be considered.

## 3.16  Plywood flexural members

In the design of plywood flexural members, the permissible stresses are found using the long-term loading grade stresses given in BS 5268: Pt 2, Tables 39 to 52 and by taking into account modification factors due to duration of loading (Table 2.1), load-sharing systems (section 3.4), exposure condition (section 3.2) and lateral stability (sections 3.11 and 3.13).

The duration of load modification factor $K3$ of Table 2.1 applies to all the stresses, with the exception of the modulus of elasticity and shear modulus.

The grade stresses given in BS 5268: Pt 2, Tables 39 to 52 are for the various plywoods as described in Table 3.5 for long-term loading in the dry exposure condition.

### Table 3.5 Dry grade stresses and moduli tables for plywoods

| | Table no. | |
| Table description | Unsanded | Sanded |
|---|---|---|
| American construction and industrial plywood: C-D grade, Exposure 1 | 39 | |
| American construction and industrial plywood: C-C grade Exposure 1 | 40 | |
| American construction and industrial plywood: A-C and B-C grades, exterior | | 41 |
| British hardwood plywood | | 42 |
| Canadian Douglas fir plywood, select tight face, select and sheathing grades | 43 | |
| Canadian Douglas fir plywood, good two sides and good one side grades | | 44 |
| Canadian softwood plywood, select tight face, select and sheathing grades | 45 | |
| Finnish birch plywood I/I, I/II, I/III, II/II, II/III, III/III, III/IV, IV/IV grades | | 46 |
| Finnish birch-faced plywood I/I, I/II, I/III, II/II, II/III, III/III, III/IV, IV/IV grades | | 47 |
| Finnish conifer plywood I/I, I/II, I/III, II/II, II/III, III/III, III/IV, IV/IV grades | | 48 |
| Swedish softwood plywood: P30 grade | 49 | 50 |
| Swedith softwood plywood: P40 grade | 51 | 52 |

Four moduli of elasticity are given in the tables, the modulus of elasticity in bending with either the face grain parallel to the span or perpendicular to the span, and the modulus of elasticity in tension and compression either parallel to the face grain or perpendicular to the face grain. There is no mean or minimum modulus of elasticity (as stated in section 3.4) for load-sharing systems.

In the wet exposure condition, the dry stresses and plywood moduli must be multiplied by the value of $K36$ as given in Table 3.6.

**Table 3.6   Modification factor $K36$ for wet exposure condition**

| Property | Value of $K36$ |
|---|---|
| Bending stress | 0.7 |
| Tension stress | 0.7 |
| Compression stress | 0.6 |
| Bearing stress (on face) | 0.6 |
| Shear stress (rolling, transverse and panel) | 0.8 |
| Modulus of elasticity | 0.9 |
| Shear modulus | 0.9 |

Source: Reproduced with permission from BS 5268: Pt 2

The section properties of the plywoods given in BS 5268: Pt 2, Tables 39 to 52 and listed in Table 3.5 are given in Tables 29 and 38. The headings of these tables are given in Table 3.7.

**Table 3.7   Section properties of plywoods**

| Table description | Table no. | |
|---|---|---|
| | Unsanded | Sanded |
| American construction and industrial plywood | 29 | 30 |
| British hardwood plywood | | 31 |
| Canadian Douglas fir and softwood plywoods | 32 | |
| Canadian Douglas fir plywood | | 33 |
| Finnish birch plywood | | 34 |
| Finnish birch faced plywood | | 35 |
| Finnish conifer plywood | | 36 |
| Swedish softwood plywood | 37 | 38 |

When carrying out calculations it does not matter whether the applied stress is parallel to or perpendicular to the face grain of the plywood as the full plywood cross-section is assumed to act with the stresses in tension, compression, bending and panel shear.

The bending stresses and moduli are used when bending is about either of the axes in the plane of the plywood, but if the panel is used as a box-beam or I-beam, then further items need to be considered. When the plywood is edge-loaded, the bending is about an axis perpendicular to its plane and the compressive stress and tensile stress due to the bending moment must be considered individually using the appropriate tension and compression stresses and moduli depending upon the face grain orientation.

Rolling shear in stressed skin panels, box-beams or I-beams need only be considered at the contact area between the framing members and the plywood. In the case of rolling shear at the web/flange junction of a plywood webbed beam and at the junction of the outermost longitudinal member and plywood cover of a stressed skin panel, there is a stress concentration modification factor, $K37 = 0.5$, which must be applied to all grade stresses of BS 5268: Pt 2, Tables 39 to 52. The lateral stability conditions of sections 3.11 and 3.13 also apply.

In calculating the deflection, both bending deflection and shear deflection must be considered. In the case of box-beams and I-beams the full cross-sectional properties of the plywood and the timber must be used.

## 3.17   Tempered hardboard flexural members

The permissible stresses for tempered hardboard flexural members are the grade stresses given in Table 3.8 and modified for duration of loading by the modification factor $K38$ as given in Table 2.1.

When the hardboard stresses are tension, compression, bending panel shear, the full cross section of the hardboard is assumed to act. For bending that is not about either of the axes in the plane of the board, but is about the axis perpendicular to the plane of the board, for example if the edge is loaded as in a built-up I-beam, the tensile and compressive stresses induced by the bending moment must be considered individually. The values of grade stresses and moduli are still those of Table 3.8.

Rolling shear in stressed skin panels, box-beams or I-beams need only be considered at the contact area between the framing members and the tempered hardboard. In the case of rolling shear at the web/flange junction of a tempered hardboard webbed beam and at the junction of the outermost longitudinal member and tempered hardboard cover of a stressed skin panel, there is a stress concentration modification factor $K37 = 0.5$ which must be applied to all the grade stresses of Table 3.8.

**Table 3.8  Dry grade stresses and moduli for TE grade tempered hardboard**

| Stress type and modulus | Value (N/mm$^2$) |
| --- | --- |
| Bending about an axis in the board plane | 4.30 |
| Tension in the board plane | 2.00 |
| Compression in board plane | 2.35 |
| Tension perpendicular to board plane | 0.08 |
| Bearing on board plane | 2.80 |
| Rolling shear | 0.35 |
| Panel shear | 1.55 |
| Modulus of elasticity | 1100 |
| Shear modulus (for panel shear) | 550 |

Source: Reproduced with permission from BS 5268: Pt 2

In determining the total deflection, the bending and shear deflection must be taken into account, together with the addition of the deflections caused separately by the long-term, net medium-term and net short- or very short-term loads appropriate to the type of member. The full cross-section properties of the tempered hardboard and timber, using the appropriate materials moduli must be used when determing the box-beam and I-beam deflections.

The lateral stability conditions of sections 3.11 and 3.13 also apply.

## 3.18  Bending moments in trussed rafter roofs

In the design of trussed rafter roofs, there are two suggested methods of analysis for bending and axial loading. Firstly, a recognized rigorous method of analysis may be used. The method must assume that all joists are pinned unless there is published information to the contrary. Secondly, there is a simplified analytical method for fully-triangulated trussed rafters.

In the simplified method, the axial forces are determined by assuming the trussed rafter is pin jointed. The bending moments are determined by assuming the members are continuous throughout their length with pinned supports at their nodes. Nodal deflection and partial joint fixity are allowed for by reducing the bending moment which will occur at the nodes with no deflection and no joint fixity, by 10 per cent. The bending moments between nodes are calculated using the reduced node moments. Bending moment coefficients, taking into account the 10 per cent reduction in node moment, are given in BS 5268: Pt 3, Table 9 for equal spans and specified loads for the node and mid-bay positions, provided the supports are as specified in Part 3, clause 42. If the trussed rafter is not supported as specified, then allowance should be made for the bending moments induced by the eccentricity of forces. If the bays are of unequal length and/or the loads are of different intensities in adjacent bays, provided all the loads on members are symmetrically located between the nodes, the difference between the mid-bay bending moments and the adjacent maximum moment may be disregarded.

## 3.19   Deflection in trussed rafter roofs

The maximum ceiling tie deflection must not exceed 0.003 times the span in the long term for the uniformly distributed dead load and imposed loads on the rafter and ceiling tie members. The ceiling tie may be pre-cambered to take account of the dead load deflection and the deflection allowance of 0.003 times the span may be applied to the uniformly distributed imposed load. If the trussed rafter is not pre-cambered for the dead load, then the deflection must not only be less than 0.003 times the span, but also less than 12 mm for trussed rafters with spans up to 12 m and 15 mm for 15 m spans. Linear interpolation of the limiting deflection is permitted for spans between 12 and 15 m.

## 3.20   Design example 1: Solid timber bearing

*Determine the permissible long-term stress and permissible long-term force for compression perpendicular to the grain for a solid timber bearing 50 mm wide, 40 mm long, positioned 200 mm from the end of the member as shown in Figure 3.3. The timber is SC5 and wane is prohibited at the bearing area.*

Grade compressive stress perpendicular to the grain SC5 
Table 8, no wane at bearing area $\left.\right\}$ 2.8 N/mm$^2$
Is the bearing located more than 75 mm from the end of the member? Yes, 200 mm.
Is the bearing less than 150 mm long? Yes, 40 mm.
Then the modification factor $K4$ must be used. Bearing length, 40 mm, using Table 3.1, $K4 = 1.33$.
Permissible long-term compressive stress perpendicular to the grain is 2.8 N/mm$^2$ × 1.33$(K4)$ = 3.72 N/mm$^2$.
Permissible long-term compressive force perpendicular to the grain is 3.72 N/mm$^2$ × 40 mm (length) × 50 mm(width) = 7.45 kN.

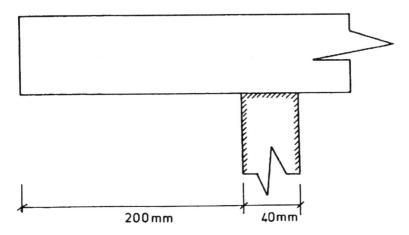

**Figure 3.3   Position of bearing**

## 3.21   Design example 2: Bearing length and effective span

*The flexural member shown in Figure 3.4 is 50 mm wide, has an effective span of 4000 mm and is supported by two bearings, each 300 mm long. The member has a total length of 5000 mm and carries a uniformly-distributed load over that length of 14.9 kN. If the permissible long-term compressive stress perpendicular to the grain for the 300 mm-long bearing is 2.8 N/mm², determine the minimum bearing length and the minimum and maximum effective span.*

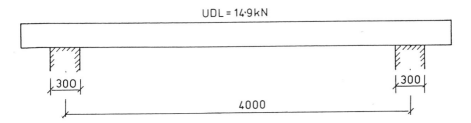

**Figure 3.4   Bearing size and effective span**

The actual bearing stress is
14.9 kN ÷ 2 ÷ 300 mm   bearing   length ÷ 50 mm   member   width   =
0.497 N/mm².

Using a 40 mm long bearing, with $K4 = 1.33$, the permissible load on the two bearings is

2.8 N/mm² × 1.33($K4$) × 40 mm long × 50 mm wide × 2 bearings = 14.9 kN

The 40 mm bearing length may be placed at any point over the 300 mm bearing length, given an effective span of between

$$\left\{ 4000 \text{ mm} - \left[ 2 \times \left( \frac{300 \text{ mm}}{2} \right) \right] \right\} + 2 \times \left( \frac{40 \text{ mm}}{2} \right) = 3740 \text{ mm}$$

or

$$\left\{ 4000 \text{ mm} + \left[ 2 \times \left( \frac{300 \text{ mm}}{2} \right) \right] \right\} - 2 \times \left( \frac{40 \text{ mm}}{2} \right) = 4260 \text{ mm}$$

as the centre line of the bearing may be placed anywhere along the 300 mm length of the supporting columns provided it is at least 20 mm in from the end of the supporting column. One advantage to be gained is that by increasing the effective span, the deflection allowed is increased from 11.22 mm (0.003 × 3740 mm) to 12.78 mm (0.003 × 4260 mm).

The bearings are located at more than 75 mm from the end of the member and do not violate any part of section 3.5 (BS 5268: Pt 2, clause 14.2). If the effective span is taken at any point other than the centre line of the supporting columns, load eccentricity on the bearing supports must be considered.

## 3.22 Design example 3: Notched beam

*The notched beam shown in Figure 3.5, is SC3, 100 mm deep and 44 mm wide. Determine its long-term shear load if a is 30 mm and $h_e$ is 50 mm.*

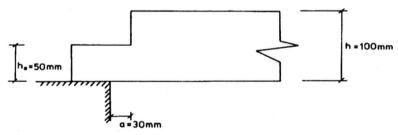

**Figure 3.5   Notched beam end**

The grade shear stress parallel to the grain (BS 5268: Pt 2, Table 8) is 0.67 N/mm² using $K5 = \dfrac{h(h_e - a) + ah_e}{h_e^2}$ as $a \leqslant h_e$ $(30 \leqslant 50)$

gives

$$K5 = \frac{100 \text{ mm } (50 \text{ mm} - 30 \text{ mm}) + (30 \text{ mm} \times 50 \text{ mm})}{50 \text{ mm}^2} = 1.4$$

giving a permissible stress of $0.67 \text{ N/mm}^2 \times 1.4(K5) = 0.938 \text{ N/mm}^2$.

The shear strength $F_v$ is found using the equation $F_v = \dfrac{2bh\tau}{3}$

where $\tau$ = permissible shear stress = $0.938 \text{ N/mm}^2$, $b$ = beam width = 44 mm, $h$ = effective depth = $h_e$ = 50 mm, and $F$ = shear load,

giving $F_v = \dfrac{2 \times 44 \text{ mm} \times 50 \text{ mm} \times 0.938 \text{ N/mm}^2}{3} = 1.376 \text{ kN}.$

Long-term shear load for the single bearing is 1.376 kN.

## 3.23 Design example 4: Solid timber floor beam

*Determine the size of a timber floor beam that will be used in a drill hall. The beams are to be spaced at 500 mm centres with an effective span of 4000 mm. The beam is of SC5, has a dead loading of 0.6 kN/m² and there is an effective means of laterally distributing the concentrated load. The bearing length is 100 mm at each end of the beam.*

Loading  1  Dead load
0.6 kN/m² × 4 m span × 0.5 m spacing = 1.2 kN UDL
     2  Imposed load
The imposed loading on a drill room, in BS 6399: Pt 1, Table 6 is 5.0 kN/m² × 4 m span × 0.5 m spacing = 10 kN UDL or 9 kN concentrated load
Long-term loading: dead load + permanently imposed load
= 1.2 kN UDL + 0 kN
= 1.2 kN UDL

Medium-term loading: (a)    dead load + temporary imposed
                              1.2 kN UDL + 10 kN UDL =
                              11.2 kN UDL, or
                  (b)    1.2 kN UDL + 9 kN concentrated load.

The concentrated load need not be considered, as the floor is capable of effective lateral distribution of the concentrated load (section 2.5.1). For example, if tongued and grooved boarding or sheet material, such as plywood or chipboard, are used as flooring.

To determine which loading is likely to produce the greatest stress and deflection, the loading is divided by the appropriate stress modification factor, $K3$ of Table 2.1.

Long-term loading, $K3 = 1.0$, giving 1.2 kN UDL ÷ 1.0 = 1.2 kN UDL
Medium-term loading, $K3 = 1.25$, giving 11.2 kN UDL ÷ 1.25 = 8.96 kN UDL

The medium-term loading is the critical loading.

The dry exposure condition grade stresses and modulus of elasticity for SC5 timber are as follows (Table 1.4):

Bending parallel to the grain                = 10 N/mm$^2$
Compression perpendicular to the grain
(No wane permitted at the bearing area) }   = 2.8 N/mm$^2$
Shear parallel to the grain                  = 1.0 N/mm$^2$
Modulus of elasticity: Minimum        = 7100 N/mm$^2$
                     Mean           = 10 700 N/mm$^2$

*Modification factors*

The medium-term duration of load modification factor $K3$ has a value of 1.25 (Table 2.1), but for imposed floor loads, $K3 = 1.0$. If the floor had been a domestic floor, with effective means of lateral distribution of concentrated loads, then the 1.4 kN concentrated floor load for domestic floors, acting over a 300 mm square, could be superimposed on the dead load. Both loads would then be treated as of medium-term duration with $K3 = 1.25$.

The floor will have four or more beams and, as they are spaced at less than 610 mm centres with adequate means of lateral load distribution, the load-sharing modification factor $K8 = 1.1$ may be used as may the mean modulus of elasticity, $E$ mean = 10 700 N/mm$^2$.

The beam size is not yet determined, but using Table 3.2 and stating that the ends of the beam will be held in position and the compression edge held in line due to the flooring, the maximum depth to breadth ratio is 5. Specifying that the SC5 timber is one of the softwoods in BS 5268: Pt 2, Table 3 and that the top and bottom edges of the beam are regularized, then BS 5268: Pt 2, Table 100 (Geometrical properties of regularized softwoods) may be used to determine the section properties.

Using the deflection criteria as the limiting factor in the design of beams, which is usually the case, an initial section size can be determined. The maximum allowable deflection is 0.003 × span = 0.003 × 4000 mm = 12 mm.

For a uniformly-distributed load, the deflection is determined by using the following equation.

$$\frac{5WL^3}{384EI,}$$

where deflection = 12 mm, $W$ = 11.2 kN, the total medium-term UDL, $E$ = 10 700 N/mm$^2$, mean modulus of elasticity, and $I$ = second moment of area, to be determined.

Rearranging the above equation and substituting the values for deflection, $W$, $L$ and $E$, we obtain:

$$I = \frac{5 \times 11\ 200 \times 4000^3}{384 \times 10\ 700 \times 12} = 72.7 \times 10^6 \text{ mm}^4.$$

Using Table 100 (BS 5268: Pt 2), ensuring the depth is no more than five times the beam width and looking down the column 'Second moment or area, about x–x' for $I$ equal to or greater than $72.7 \times 10^6$ mm$^4$, the first $I$ value obtained is $I = 91.9 \times 10^6$ mm$^4$. There are other possible section sizes given in the table, but they all have larger cross-sections and would increase cost.

For $I = 91.9 \times 10^6$ mm$^4$, the section size is 75 × 245 mm and would give a bending deflection of

$$\frac{5 \times 11\ 200 \times 4000^3}{384 \times 10\ 700 \times 91.9 \times 10^6} = 9.49 \text{ mm}.$$

The depth to breadth ratio is 245/75 = 3.27 which is less than 5.

The additional deflection due to shear is found as follows:

$$\frac{3WL}{20 \times G \times b \times d}$$

where $W$ = 11 200 N, the UDL, $L$ = 4000 mm, effective span, $G$ = shear modulus = ($E$ mean × 1/16) = 669 N/mm$^2$, $b$ = beam width = 75 mm, and $d$ = beam depth = 245 mm, giving the shear deflection as

$$\frac{3 \times 11\,200 \times 4000}{20 \times 669 \times 75 \times 245} = 0.55 \text{ mm.}$$

Total deflection = bending deflection + shear deflection
= 9.49 mm + 0.55 mm
= 10.04 mm which is less than the allowable deflection of 12 mm.

If a non-standard size of section were to be used, the minimum section size, assuming $d = 5b$ and adding together the bending and shear deflection, would be 53 × 265 mm. This would give a deflection of 11.33 mm. The section would also require checking for permissible stresses.

Returning to the standard section size of 75 × 245 mm, the depth modification factor $K7 = \left(\dfrac{300}{245}\right)^{0.11} = 1.0225$.

The permissible stresses are as follows:
Bending parallel to the grain:
10 N/mm$^2$ × 1.1($K8$) × 1.25($K3$) × 1.0225($K7$) = 14.01 N/mm$^2$.
The depth modification factor $K7$ only applies to the grade bending stress.
Compression perpendicular to the grain:
2.8 N/mm$^2$ × 1.1($K8$) × 1.25($K3$) = 3.85 N/mm$^2$.
Shear parallel to the grain:
1.0 N/mm$^2$ × 1.1($K8$) × 1.25($K3$) = 1.375 N/mm$^2$.

The maximum bending moment in the beam is $M = \dfrac{WL}{8}$

$$M = \frac{11\,200 \text{ N} \times 4000 \text{ mm}}{8} = 5.6 \times 10^6 \text{ N/mm}$$

The applied bending stress is $\sigma = M/Z$ where $Z$ = section modulus = 750 × 10$^3$ mm$^3$, giving

$$\sigma = \frac{5.6 \times 10^6 \text{ N/mm}}{750 \times 10^3 \text{ mm}^3} = 7.47 \text{ N/mm}^2.$$

The applied bending stress of 7.47 N/mm$^2$ is less than the permissible bending stress of 14.06 N/mm$^2$, therefore satisfactory.

*Shear stress at the support*

The maximum applied shear stress at a support is found from the following equation:

$$\frac{3F}{2\,bd,}$$

where $F$ = support load = 11 200 N ÷ number of supports = 5600 N, $b$ = beam width = 75 mm, and $d$ = beam depth = 245 mm.

$$\text{Shear stress} = \frac{3 \times 5600 \text{ N}}{2 \times 75 \text{ mm} \times 245 \text{ mm}} = 0.457 \text{ N/mm}^2$$

The applied shear stress of 0.457 N/mm² is less than the permissible shear stress of 1.375 N/mm², therefore satisfactory.

*Bearing stress at the supports*

The bearing length is 100 mm at the ends of the beam. The bearing stress on the side grain of the timber is

$$\frac{5600 \text{ N}}{100 \text{ mm bearing length} \times 75 \text{ mm bearing width}} = 0.747 \text{ N/mm}^2.$$

No wane at the bearing areas.
   The applied compressive stress perpendicular to the grain is 0.747 N/mm² which is less than the permissible compressive stress perpendicular to the grain of 3.85 N/mm², therefore satisfactory.

## 3.24   Design example 5: Horizontally-glued laminated roof beam

*A horizontally-glued laminated whitewood, grade LB timber roof beam, is to have an effective span of 10 metres. The ends of the beam will be held in position and the beam will be held in line as by purlins and tie-rods. If the total dead load is 20 kN and the imposed load is 30 kN, determine the beam size. The bearing length is 150 mm.*

*Deflection*

It is usual, when designing glued laminated beams, to pre-camber the beam to take account of the total dead load deflection. The deflection

**49**

used in the section size determination is the total imposed load deflection, which is limited to 0.003 × effective span. Deflection = 0.003 × 10 000 mm = 30 mm.

To determine the section size we use the following:

$$\text{deflection} = 30 \text{ mm} = \frac{5WL^3}{384EI}$$

where $W$ = 30 000 N, the imposed load,
$L$ = 10 000 mm the effective span,
$E$ = SS grade mean modulus of elasticity (section 6.2) × $K20$ (Table 24)
= 10 500 N/mm$^2$ Table 10, SS grade whitewood) × 1.05($K20$)
= 11 025 N/mm$^2$

rearranging the equation to determine $I$ as follows:

$$I = \frac{5 \times W \times L^3}{384 \times E \times 30 \text{ mm}} = \frac{5 \times 30\,000 \text{ N} \times (10\,000)^3}{384 \times 11\,025 \text{ N/mm}^2 \times 30 \text{ mm}}$$
$$= 1.181 \times 10^9 \text{ mm}^4.$$

The minimum second moment of area to ensure the bending deflection of less than 30 mm is 1.181 × 10$^9$ mm$^4$.

The beam will be held in line as by purlins and tie-rods. Using Table 3.2, the maximum depth to breadth ratio is 4.

Using $I = bd^3/12 = 1.181 \times 10^9$ mm$^4$ and $d/4 = b$, where $d$ = beam depth and $b$ = beam width, the minimum beam size is determined as $b$ = 122 mm and $d$ = 488 mm.

There are no standard sizes of whitewood laminations but lamination sizes of 45 and 33.3 mm machined from 50 and 38 mm whitewood are often used.

Using No. 12 45 mm laminations will give a beam depth of 540 mm. Keeping the beam width to 25 per cent of the depth will give a final beam size of 540 × 135 mm.

Checking the total beam deflections as follows:

$$\text{Bending deflection} = \frac{5WL^3}{384EI}$$

where $I = \dfrac{135 \times 540^3}{12} = 1.772 \times 10^9$ mm$^4$ gives

$$\frac{5 \times 30\,000 \text{ N} \times (10\,000 \text{ mm})^3}{384 \times 11\,025 \text{ N/mm}^2 \times 1.772 \times 10^9 \text{ mm}^4} = 20.00 \text{ mm}.$$

$$\text{Shear deflection} = \frac{3WL}{20 \times G \times b \times d}$$

where $G$ = shear modulus = $E \div 16$ (section 1.8) = 689 N/mm$^2$ gives

$$\frac{3 \times 30\,000 \times 10\,000}{20 \times 689 \times 135 \times 540} = 0.896 \text{ mm.}$$

The total deflection due to bending and shear is 20.00 mm + 0.896 mm = 20.896 mm, which is less than the permissible total deflection of 30 mm, therefore satisfactory.

It is possible to use No. 11 45 mm laminations which would give a beam depth of 495 mm and a beam width of 125 mm. The bending deflection would be 28.04 mm and the shear deflection 1.06 mm giving a total deflection of 29.10 mm.

The amount of pre-camber to be given to the beam to offset the total dead load deflection is found by adding together the bending and shear dead load deflection as follows:

$$\text{Total deflection} = \frac{5WL^3}{384EI} + \frac{3WL}{20 \times G \times b \times d}$$

where $W$ = 20 000 N, giving a total deflection

$$\frac{5 \times 20\,000 \text{ N} \times (10\,000 \text{ mm})^3}{384 \times 11\,025 \text{ N/mm}^2 \times 1.772 \times 10^9 \text{ mm}^4} +$$

$$\frac{3 \times 20\,000 \text{ N} \times 10\,000 \text{ mm}}{20 \times 689 \text{ N/mm}^2 \times 135 \text{ mm} \times 540 \text{ mm}}$$

$$= 13.33 + 0.60 = 13.93 \text{ mm.}$$

Minimum required pre-camber is 13.93 mm.

*Stresses*

Using BS 5268: Pt 2, Table 10, the SS grade whitewood grade stresses are as follows:

Bending parallel to the grain = 7.5 N/mm$^2$.
Compression perpendicular to the grain = 2.1 N/mm$^2$ if wane is permitted at the bearing area, but as wane is not permitted in the laminating grades of timber the compression perpendicular to the grain may be increased by 33 per cent to 2.1 N/mm$^2$ × 1.33 = 2.793 N/mm$^2$.

**51**

Shear parallel to the grain = 0.82 N/mm$^2$.

Permissible bending stress = 7.5 N/mm$^2$ × $K3$ × $K7$ × $K15$, where $K3$ = 1.25, the duration of load modification factor for the medium-term load of dead load plus imposed load (section 2.2), $K7$ = the depth modification factor (section 3.9)

$$= \frac{0.81 \ (h^2 + 92 \ 300)}{(h^2 + 56 \ 800)}$$

where $h$ = beam depth = 540 mm

$$= \frac{0.81 \ (540^2 + 92 \ 300)}{(540^2 + 56 \ 800)} = 0.893.$$

$K15$ = modification factor for bending parallel to the grain, for LB grade with 12 laminations = 1.43 (BS 5268: Pt 2, Table 24).

Permissible bending stresses = 7.5 N/mm$^2$ × 1.25($K3$) × 0.893($K7$) × 1.43($K15$)
$$= 11.97 \ \text{N/mm}^2.$$

*Applied bending stress*

The applied bending stress is found from $\sigma = My/I$ where $M$ = applied dead plus imposed load bending moment.

$$\frac{WL}{8} = \frac{50 \ 000 \ \text{N} \times 10 \ 000 \ \text{mm}}{8} = 62.5 \times 10^6 \ \text{Nmm}$$

$W$ = dead + imposed load = 20 kN + 30 kN = 50 kN, $I$ = second moment of area

$$= \frac{bd^3}{12} = 1.772 \times 10^9 \ \text{mm}^4$$

$$y = \frac{d}{2} = 270 \ \text{mm}$$

giving $\sigma = \dfrac{62.5 \times 10^6 \ \text{Nmm} \times 270 \ \text{mm}}{1.772 \times 10^9 \ \text{mm}^4} = 9.523 \ \text{N/mm}^2.$

The applied bending stress of 9.523 N/mm$^2$ is less than the permissible bending stress of 11.91 N/mm$^2$, therefore satisfactory.

The end joints in LB laminations must have an efficiency rating of at least 70 per cent (section 6.3 (BS 5268: Pt 2, Appendix F)) and in accordance with Table 104 of BS 5268: Pt 2. The finger profile length must be either 50 or 55 mm.

*Permissible shear stress*

The permissible shear stress is 0.82 N/mm$^2$ × $K3$ × $K19$, where $K19$ is the modification factor for shear parallel to the grain for LB grade glued laminated members, with 12 laminations and is taken from BS 5268: Pt 2, Table 22, giving $K19$ = 2.0. The permissible shear stress becomes: 0.82 N/mm$^2$ × 1.25($K3$) × 2.0($K19$) = 2.05 N/mm$^2$.

*Applied shear stress*

The applied shear stress = $3F/2bd$ where $F$ = the support load of 50 000 N ÷ 2 supports = 25 000 N, $b$ = the beam width of 135 mm, and $d$ = the beam depth of 540 mm, giving

$$\frac{3 \times 25\ 000}{2 \times 135 \times 540} = 0.514 \text{ N/mm}^2$$

The applied shear stress of 0.514 N/mm$^2$ is less than the permissible shear stress of 2.05 N/mm$^2$, therefore satisfactory.

*Compression perpendicular to the grain*

No wane is allowed at the bearing. The bearing load is $F$ = 25 000 N, with a bearing width of 135 mm.

The permissible bearing stress = 2.793 N/mm$^2$ × $K3$ × $K18$, where $K18$ = 1.33 from BS 5268: Pt 2, Table 24, giving 2.793 N/mm$^2$ × 1.25($K3$) × 1.33($K18$) = 4.64 N/mm$^2$.

The minimum bearing length

$$= \frac{F}{b \times \text{permissible stress}} = \frac{25\ 000 \text{ N}}{135 \text{ mm} \times 3.715 \text{ N/mm}^2} = 49.85 \text{ mm}$$

The minimum bearing length of 49.85 mm is less than the actual bearing length of 150 mm, therefore satisfactory.

## 3.25 Design example 6: A plywood box-beam cat-walk

*The plywood box-beam shown in Figure 3.6 is to be used as the main structural member of a cat-walk. The dead load supported by the box-beam includes the necessary load spreading timbers and totals 450 N per metre run of the beam. The effective span is 7 metres. If the flanges are of SC4 timber and the webs are of British hardwood plywood, with the face grain horizontal, check that the proposed design is satisfactory.*

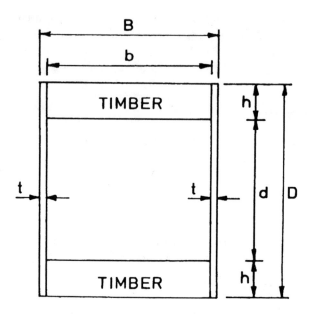

**Figure 3.6  Section through the plywood box-beam**
B = 193 mm, b = 169 mm, h = 47 mm, D = 350 mm, d = 256 mm and t = 12 mm. Timber size from BS 5268: Pt 2, Table 99, 169 × 47 mm.

*Loading*

The dead load is 0.45 kN/m × 7 metre span = 3.15 kN. The imposed load for a cat-walk is a concentrated load of 1 kN at 1 m centres as shown in Figure 3.7. The bending moment due to the dead load is

$$\frac{WL}{8} = \frac{3.15 \text{ kN} \times 7 \text{ m}}{8} = 2.756 \text{ kNm}.$$

The bending moment due to the imposed load may be determined in one of three ways. The load may start at the support at 1 m intervals, and by taking moments about the beam span centre line gives a bending moment of 6 kNm. The load may start half a metre to the right of the left-hand support, with a load at the centre, as shown in Figure 3.7, giving a bending moment of 6.25 kNm.

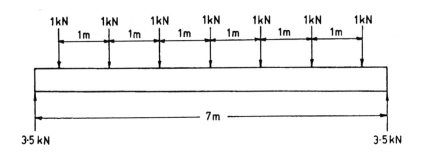

**Figure 3.7   Worst loading condition for the imposed load**

The 7 kN concentrated loads as shown in Figure 3.7 could also be considered as a UDL of 7 kN giving a bending moment of

$$\frac{WL}{8} = \frac{7kN \times 7m}{8} = 6.125 \text{ kNm.}$$

The largest bending moment of 6.25 kNm will be used.

The worst load combination will be the medium-term loading (section 2.14) of dead load bending moment + imposed load bending moment of 2.756 kN + 6.25 kNm = 9.006 kNm.

The duration of load modification factor of $K3$ is 1.25 (sections 2.2 and 2.14) and is applicable to all strength properties, but not to the elastic or shear moduli.

The box-beam is a single beam and there is no load sharing (section 2.8).

*Materials*

It is suggested that British hardwood plywood, with its face grain horizontal, i.e. face grain parallel to the span, should be used and that it should have a nominal thickness of 12 mm. The dry grade stresses are given in BS 5268: Pt 2, Table 42, as follows:

| | | |
|---|---|---|
| Extreme fibre in bending | = | 15.7 N/mm² |
| Tension | = | 8.25 N/mm² |
| Compression | = | 8.55 N/mm² |

**55**

| Rolling shear | = | 0.69 N/mm² |
|---|---|---|
| Panel shear | = | 2.71 N/mm² |
| $E$ in tension and compression | = | 7400 N/mm² |
| Shear modulus | = | 580 N/mm² |

The box-beam must be designed as a built-up beam (section 3.13, BS 5268: Pt 2, clause 14.10) using BS 5268: Pt 2, Table 26 and the modification factors $K27$, $K28$ and $K29$. This means that the SS grade stresses must be used for the timber and that it must be also a SC4 timber as originally specified. Table 3 of BS 5268: Pt 2 gives the timber species and grade that are also in SC4. The SS grade whitewood is chosen and the grade stresses taken from Table 10 of BS 5268: Pt 2, and are used as follows:

| Bending parallel to the grain | = | 7.5 N/mm² |
|---|---|---|
| Tension parallel to the grain | = | 4.5 N/mm² |
| Compression parallel to the grain | = | 7.9 N/mm² |
| Shear parallel to the grain | = | 0.82 N/mm² |
| Minimum modulus of elasticity | = | 7000 N/mm² |

The minimum modulus of elasticity is used as the box-beam is not part of a load-sharing system.

The grade stresses for bending and tension are for timber 300 mm deep and will be modified using the modification factors $K7$ for bending and $K14$ for tension.

The values of $K27$, $K28$ and $K29$ in BS 5268: Pt 2, Table 26 are determined as follows:

The number of pieces of timber in each flange is taken as the number of laminations, and using Figure 3.6 is 1 for each flange, giving $K27 = K28 = K29 = 1$ for the stresses.

The value of $K28$ to be applied to the minimum modulus of elasticity for deflection calculations depends upon the total number of pieces of timber in both flanges, which from Figure 3.6 is 2, giving $K28 = 1.14$.

The modulus of elasticity for deflection calculations is 7000 N/mm² × 1.14($K28$) = 7980 N/mm².

The compression perpendicular to the grain modification factor $K29$ is 1, but if no wane is permitted, $K29 = 1.33$.

In the case of box-beams, and any other composite beam made of more than one material, it is assumed that they are all rigidly connected and that the strain at the common surfaces will be the same. Each material has its own limiting stresses and modulus of elasticity and it is necessary to determine which material is the limiting material, and transform all sections to the equivalent section of the limiting material.

At any common surface the strain is equal for both materials giving

$$\text{Strain} = \left(\frac{\sigma}{E}\right)_{\text{timber}} = \left(\frac{\sigma}{E}\right)_{\text{plywood}}$$

## Timber

The timber is not being bent, but is resisting the load by compression and tension.

Permissible compression flange stress = 7.9 N/mm$^2$ × $K3$ × $K28$ giving 7.9 N/mm$^2$ × 1.25 ($K3$) × 1.0 ($K28$) = 9.875 N/mm$^2$.
Permissible tension flange stress = 4.5 N/mm$^2$ × $K3$ × $K27$

where $K14$ = width modification factor (BS 5268: Pt 2, clauses 5.6, 16.2) = $(300/h)^{0.11}$ where $h$ = timber width = 169 mm, and $K14 = (300/169)^{0.11} = 1.0652$, giving 4.5 N/mm$^2$ × 1.25($K3$) × 1.0652($K14$) × 1.0($K27$) = 5.9918 N/mm$^2$.
   The maximum permissible timber strain is found by taking the lowest of the compressive or tension stresses and dividing by the minimum $E$ value as follows:

$$\frac{5.9918 \text{ N/mm}^2}{7000 \text{ N/mm}^2} = 855.96 \times 10^{-6}$$

## Plywood

When the plywood is bent about an axis, in its plane, the bending stresses and moduli are used. In the case of built-up beams where bending is about an axis perpendicular to the plane of the plywood, the tensile and compressive stresses and moduli should be used.

Permissible compressive stress = 8.55 N/mm$^2$ × 1.25($K3$) = 10.688 N/mm$^2$.
Permissible tensile stress = 8.25 N/mm$^2$ × 1.25 ($K3$) = 10.313 N/mm$^2$.
Maximum permissible plywood strain is

$$\frac{10.313 \text{ N/mm}^2}{7400 \text{ N/mm}^2} = 1393.6 \times 10^{-6}$$

The timber strain of 855.96 × 10$^{-6}$ is lower than the plywood strain of 1393.6 × 10$^{-6}$ and is the limiting strain. The plywood is to be changed to an equivalent timber thickness as follows:

Equivalent timber thickness = plywood thickness $\times \dfrac{\text{plywood } E \text{ modulus}}{\text{timber } E \text{ modulus}}$

$$= \frac{12 \text{ mm} \times 7400 \text{ N/mm}^2}{7000 \text{ N/mm}^2} = 12.686 \text{ mm.}$$

The limiting medium-term stress is the timber tension flange stress of 5.9918 N/mm².

*Deflection*

The total permissible deflection due to bending and shear effects is limited to 0.003 × effective span (section 3.10, BS 5268: Pt 2, clause 14.7) = 0.003 × 7000 mm = 21 mm.

Treating the imposed load as a UDL of 7 kN and adding to it the dead load UDL of 3.15 kN gives a total load $W$ of 10.15 kN. The deflection due to bending

$$= \frac{5WL^3}{384EI}$$

where  $W$ = 10.15 kN
$E$ = 7000 N/mm² × 1.14 ($K28$) = 7980 N/mm²
$B$ = 169 mm + 2 × (12.686) = 194.37 mm
$D$ = 350 mm
$L$ = effective span of 7000 mm
$I$ = $I$ for the transformed section = $\dfrac{BD^3}{12} - \dfrac{bd^3}{12}$
$b$ = 169 mm
$d$ = 350 − (2 × 47) = 256 mm.

$$I, \text{transformed section} = \frac{194.37 \times 350^3}{12} - \frac{169 \times 256^3}{12}$$
$$= 458.19 \times 10^6 \text{ mm}^4.$$

$$\text{Bending deflection} = \frac{5 \times 10\ 150 \text{ N} \times (7000 \text{ mm})^3}{384 \times 7980 \text{ N/mm}^2 \times 458.19 \times 10^6}$$
$$= 12.398 \text{ mm.}$$

The deflection due to shear = $WL/8Cbd$
where the shearing forces are uniformly distributed over the web area $bd$,

$W$ = 10.15 kN
$L$ = 7000 mm

$b$ = 2 × 12.686 = 25.372 mm, the transformed thickness of the two outer plywood webs

$d$ = 350 − (2 × 47) = 256 mm

$C$ = modulus of rigidity of the transformed section

= plywood modulus of elasticity $\times \dfrac{E_{\text{timber}}}{E_{\text{plywood}}}$

= 580 N/mm$^2$ × $\dfrac{7980 \text{ N/mm}^2}{7400 \text{ N/mm}^2}$ = 625.46 N/mm$^2$.

$$\text{Shear deflection} = \frac{10\ 150 \text{ N} \times 7000 \text{ mm}}{8 \times 625.46 \text{ N/mm}^2 \times 25.372 \text{ mm} \times 256 \text{ mm}}$$

$$= 2.186 \text{ mm}.$$

Total deflection = 12.398 + 2.186 = 14.584 mm.
The total deflection of 14.584 mm is less than the permissible deflection of 21 mm, therefore satisfactory.

*Bending stresses*

Treating the imposed load as a UDL, the applied bending moment is due to the dead load and the imposed load as follows:

2.756 kNm + 6.25 kNm = 9.006 kNm = $M$.

Using applied stress $My/I$ where $I$ = 458.19 × 10$^6$ mm$^4$ for the transformed section and $y$ = 350 ÷ 2 = 175 mm, gives

$$\frac{9.006 \text{ kNm} \times 175 \text{ mm}}{458.19 \times 10^6 \text{ mm}^4} = 3.440 \text{ N/mm}^2$$

The stress due to bending of 3.44 N/mm$^2$ is less than the allowable tension stress of 5.99 N/mm$^2$, therefore satisfactory.

*Panel shear*

Permissible panel shear = 2.71 N/mm$^2$ × 1.25($K3$) = 3.388 N/mm$^2$.
   The horizontal shear stress in the plywood webs is called the panel shear and is found using the following equation:

$$\frac{VQ}{tI_{\text{xx}}}$$

where

$V$ = maximum shearing force on the beam = 10.15 kN ÷ 2 = 5.075 kN.

$Q$ = first moment of inertia of the area above the x–x axis, of transformed section as follows

$$Q = \left[169 \times 47\left(\frac{350}{2} - \frac{47}{2}\right) \text{ for the timber}\right]$$
$$+ \left[2 \times 12.686 \times \frac{350}{2} \times \frac{350}{4} \text{ for the plywood}\right]$$

$Q$ = $1.5919 \times 10^6$ mm$^3$

$t$ = transformed web thickness = $2 \times 12.686$ mm = 25.372 mm

$I_{xx}$ = $458.19 \times 10^6$ mm$^4$

giving the applied panel shear as

$$\frac{5075 \text{ N} \times 1.5919 \times 10^6 \text{ mm}^3}{25.372 \text{ mm} \times 458.19 \times 10^6 \text{ mm}^4} = 0.695 \text{ N/mm}^2.$$

The applied panel shear stress of 0.695 N/mm$^2$ is less than the permissible panel shear stress of 3.388 N/mm$^2$, therefore satisfactory.

*Rolling shear*

Rolling shear is considered at the junction of the web and flange of a plywood webbed box-beam, with the grade stess being multiplied by the stress concentration modification factor $K37 = 0.5$.

Permissible rolling shear = 0.69 N/mm$^2$ × 1.25 ($K3$) × 0.5 ($K37$) = 0.431 N/mm$^2$.

Applied rolling shear stress = $\dfrac{VQ_f}{hI}$,

where

$V$ = maximum shearing force on the beam = 5.075 kN

$Q_f$ = first moment of area of the flange above the neutral axis x–x

$$= \left(169 \times 47 \left(\frac{350}{2} - \frac{47}{2}\right)\right) = 1.2034 \times 10^6 \text{ mm}^3$$

$h$ = the depth of area over which the plywood web is glued to the timber flange = $2 \times h = 2 \times 47$ mm = 94 mm

$I$ = $458.19 \times 10^6$ mm$^4$,

giving the applied rolling shear as

$$\frac{5075 \text{ N} \times 1.2034 \times 10^6 \text{ mm}^3}{94 \text{ mm} \times 458.19 \times 10^6 \text{ mm}^4} = 0.142 \text{ N/mm}^2$$

The applied rolling shear of $0.142 \text{ N/mm}^2$ is less than the allowable rolling shear of $0.431 \text{ N/mm}^2$, therefore satisfactory.

Three further design checks need to be made:

1 The applied compressive stress perpendicular to the grain at the bearing must be checked as in section 3.5 (clause 14.2).
2 Web stiffness may be needed to ensure strength and stability at all points of concentrated load and at the bearings. This is to ensure the imposed load on the beam has been adequately distributed.
3 The lateral stability must be checked in accordance with section 3.13 (clause 14.10).

To determine the ratio of $\dfrac{I_{xx}}{I_{yy}}$ of the transformed section where

$$I_{xx} = 458.19 \times 10^6 \text{ mm}^4$$

$$I_{yy} = \frac{DB^3}{12} - \frac{db^3}{12} = \frac{350 \times 194.37^3}{12} - \frac{256 \times 169^3}{12}$$

$$= 111.21 \times 10^6 \text{ mm}^4$$

giving

$$\frac{I_{xx}}{I_{yy}} = \frac{458.19 \times 10^6}{111.21 \times 10^6} = 4.1202.$$

The ratio of 4.1202 is less than 5 and no lateral support is required.

## 3.26 Design example 7: A tempered hardboard box-beam cat-walk

*The tempered hardboard box-beam shown in Figure 3.8 is to be used as the main structural member of a cat-walk. The dead load includes the necessary load spreading timbers and total 450 N per metre run of the beam. The effective span is 5 metres. If the flanges are of SS grade whitewood and the webs are of TE grade tempered hardboard, check that the proposed design is satisfactory.*

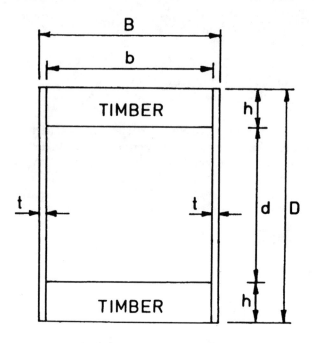

**Figure 3.8   Section through the tempered hardboard box-beam**
B = 185 mm, b = 169 mm, h = 47 mm, D = 350 mm, d = 256 mm and
t = 8 mm nominal, 7.3 minimum. Timber size 169 × 47 mm, from BS 5268:
Pt 2, Table 99.

*Loading*

The dead load is 0.45 kN/m × 5 m span = 2.25 kN.

The imposed load for a cat-walk is a concentrated load of 1 kN at 1 m
centres as shown in Figure 3.9.

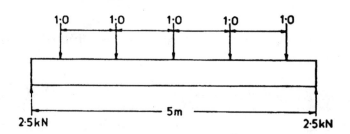

**Figure 3.9   Imposed loading on the tempered hardboard box-beam**

Dead load bending moment

$$\frac{WL}{8} = \frac{2.25 \text{ kN} \times 5 \text{ m}}{8} = 1.406 \text{ kNm}$$

The worst imposed load positioning is as shown in Figure 3.9 with the first 1 kN load starting half a metre from the left-hand support. By taking moments about the centre line, the maximum imposed bending load bending moment is 3.25 kNm.

The duration of load modification factor $K38$ for tempered hardboard is 1.0 for long-term loading and 1.50 for medium-term loading (section 2.2 (clause 36)). When a value of $K38$ other than 1.0 is used, the design must be checked for all other conditions of loading.

The value of $K28$, to be applied to the minimum modulus of elasticity for deflection calculations, depends upon the total number of pieces of timber in both flanges which is 2, giving $K28 = 1.14$.

The modulus of elasticity for deflection calculations is 7000 N/mm$^2$ × 1.14($K28$) = 7980 N/mm$^2$.

As there will not be any wane present in the whitewood flanges, $K29 = 1.33$ (Table 26).

In the case of box-beams and any other composite beam, it is assumed that the materials are rigidly connected together and that the strain at the common surface will be the same. Each material has its own limiting stress and modulus of elasticity and it is necessary to determine which material is the limiting material:

$$\text{Strain} = \left(\frac{\text{stress}}{\text{Youngs modulus}}\right)_{\text{timber}} = \left(\frac{\text{stress}}{\text{Youngs modulus}}\right)_{\text{hardboard}}$$

*Timber*

The whitewood flanges are not being bent, but are resisting the load by compression and tension.

Permissible compression flange stress = 7.9 N/mm$^2$ × $K3$ × $K28$ giving 7.9 N/mm$^2$ × 1.25($K3$) × 1.0($K28$) = 9.875 N/mm$^2$.

Permissible tension flange stress = 4.5 N/mm$^2$ × $K3$ × $K14$ × $K27$ where $K14$ = width modification factor (section 5.6 (clause 16.2))

$$= \left(\frac{300}{h}\right)^{0.11}$$

where $h$ = timber width = 169 mm$^2$

$$= \left(\frac{300}{169}\right)^{0.11} = 1.0652$$

giving

$$4.5 \text{ N/mm}^2 \times 1.25(K3) \times 1.0652(K14) \times 1.0(K27) = 5.992 \text{ N/mm}^2.$$

The tension stress of 5.992 N/mm$^2$ is less than the compression stress of 9.875 N/mm$^2$, giving a limiting strain of

$$\frac{5.99 \text{ N/mm}^2}{7000 \text{ N/mm}^2} = 855.96 \times 10^{-6} \text{ using the minimum } E.$$

*Tempered hardboard*

In the design of the box-beam, it is necessary to determine the correct hardboard modulus of elasticity, which varies according to the ratios of applied to permissible stress for each load duration. To determine the correct value of the stress ratio, it may be necessary to carry out a series of iterative calculations. In the following claculation only the last iteration is shown to save space.

For long-term loading assume a stress ratio of 0.155 (Table 57) which gives $K39 = 2.96$. The long-term load $E$ value = 1100 N/mm$^2 \times$ 2.96($K39$) = 3256 N/mm$^2$. Minimum timber $E$ value = 7000 N/mm$^2$, giving a transformed hardboard thickness of

$$7.3 \text{ mm} \times \frac{3256 \text{ N/mm}^2}{7000 \text{ N/mm}^2} = 3.40 \text{ mm.}$$

Using applied stress = $My/I \times$ the modular ratio, where $M = 1.406$ kNm, the dead load bending moment $y = D \div 2 = 350 \div 2 = 175$ mm, and

$$I = \frac{BD^3}{12} - \frac{bd^3}{12} \text{ for the transformed section}$$

$$\frac{(169 + (2 \times 3.40)) \times 350^3}{12} - \frac{169 \times 256^3}{12} = 391.84 \times 10^6 \text{ mm}^4$$

giving applied stress

$$= \frac{1.406 \times 10^6 \text{ Nmm} \times 175 \text{ mm}}{391.84 \times 10^6 \text{ mm}^4} \times \frac{3256 \text{ N/mm}^2}{7000 \text{ N/mm}^2} = 0.2921 \text{ N/mm}^2.$$

The limiting permissible stress in the hardboard is the tension stress of $2.00 \text{ N/mm}^2$, which when multiplied by the modification factor $K38$ gives a permissible long-term dead load stress of $2.00 \text{ N/mm}^2 \times 1.0$ $(K38) = 2.00 \text{ N/mm}^2$.

The applied stress to permissible stress ratio is

$$\frac{0.2921 \text{ N/mm}^2}{2.00 \text{ N/mm}^2} = 0.15.$$

The hardboard strain is

$$\frac{0.2921 \text{ N/mm}^2}{3256 \text{ N/mm}^2} = 89.71 \times 10^{-6}$$

which is less than the maximum timber strain of $855.96 \times 10^{-6}$, therefore satisfactory.

For the net medium loads, a stress ratio of 0.25 is assumed, giving $K40 = 3.375$ (Table 57) and a medium-term $E$ value of $1100 \text{ N/mm}^2 \times 3.375(K40) = 3713 \text{ N/mm}^2$, and a transformed hardboard thickness of

$$7.3 \text{ mm} \times \frac{3713 \text{ N/mm}^2}{7000 \text{ N/mm}^2} = 3.872 \text{ mm}.$$

For the net medium-term load which refers to the loads of the duration stated and excludes any other loads of longer duration, we have

$M = 3.25 \text{ kNm}$
$y = 175 \text{ mm}$

$$I = \frac{(169 \times (2 \times 3.872)) \times 350^3}{12} - \frac{169 \times 256^3}{12} = 395.21 \times 10^6 \text{ mm}^4$$

giving an applied stress of

$$\frac{3.25 \times 10^6 \text{ Nmm} \times 175 \text{ mm}}{395.21 \times 10^6 \text{ mm}^4} \times \frac{3713 \text{ N/mm}^2}{7000 \text{ N/mm}^2} = 0.763 \text{ N/mm}^2.$$

The limiting permissible tensile stress is $2.00 \text{ N/mm}^2 \times 1.5(K38) = 3.00 \text{ N/mm}^2$ giving a net medium-term stress ratio of

$$\frac{0.763 \text{ N/mm}^2}{3.00 \text{ N/mm}^2} = 0.25.$$

The hardboard strain is $\dfrac{0.763 \text{ N/mm}^2}{3713 \text{ N/mm}^2} = 205.49 \times 10^{-6}$

which is less than the maximum timber strain of $855.96 \times 10^6$, therefore satisfactory.

The total hardboard strain of $295.19 \times 10^{-6}$ ($89.71 \times 10^{-6}$ + $205.49 \times 10^{-6}$) is less than the maximum timber strain, therefore satisfactory.

*Panel shear*

The panel shear in the hardboard must be checked for both long-term and net medium-term loadings using panel shear stress = $VQ/tI$, where $V$ = shearing force, $Q$ = first moment of area of the section above the NA, $I$ = second moment of area of the transformed section, and $t$ = untransformed web thickness.

For the long-term loading

$$
\begin{aligned}
V &= 2.25 \text{ kN} \div 2 = 1125 \text{ N} \\
Q &= \{169 \times 47 \times [(350 \div 2) - (47 \div 2)]\} + 2 \times \{[(175 \div 2) \times 175] \\
&\quad \times 3.4\} \\
&= 1.3075 \times 10^6 \text{ mm}^3 \\
I &= 391.84 \times 10^6 \text{ mm}^4 \\
t &= 2 \times 7.3 \text{ mm} = 14.6 \text{ mm}
\end{aligned}
$$

giving panel shear stress

$$\frac{1125 \text{ N} \times 1.3075 \times 10^6 \text{ mm}^3}{391.84 \times 10^6 \text{ mm}^4 \times 14.6 \text{ mm}} = 0.257 \text{ N/mm}^2.$$

Allowable panel shear = $1.55 \text{ N/mm}^2 \times 1(K39) = 1.55 \text{ N/mm}^2$.

The long-term applied panel shear of $0.257 \text{ N/mm}^2$ is less than the permissible panel shear of $1.55 \text{ N/mm}^2$, therefore satisfactory.

For medium-term loading

$$
\begin{aligned}
V &= 5 \text{ kN} \div 2 = 2500 \text{ N} \\
Q &= \{169 \times 47 \times [(350 \div 2) - (47 \div 2)]\} + 2 \times \{[(175 \div 2) \times 175] \\
&\quad \times 3.872\} \\
&= 1.322 \times 10^6 \text{ mm}^3 \\
I &= 395.21 \times 10^6 \text{ mm}^4 \\
t &= 2 \times 7.3 \text{ mm} = 14.6 \text{ mm}
\end{aligned}
$$

giving panel shear

$$\frac{2500 \text{ N} \times 1.322 \times 10^6 \text{ mm}^3}{395.21 \times 10^6 \text{ mm}^4 \times 14.6 \text{ mm}} = 0.573 \text{ N/mm}^2.$$

Permissible panel shear = $1.55 \text{ N/mm}^2 \times 1.50(K38) = 2.325 \text{ N/mm}^2$.

The loaded net medium-term panel shear of $0.573 \ N/mm^2$ plus the loaded long-term panel shear of $0.257 \ N/mm^2$ totals $0.830 \ N/mm^2$ and is less than the permissible panel shear of $2.325 \ N/mm^2$, therefore satisfactory.

## Rolling shear

Only the area of contact between the hardboard and the timber flange members can be considered in calculating rolling shear. A stress concentration factor $K37 = 0.5$ must be applied to the grade stresses.

The calculation for rolling shear uses the same equation as panel shear except that $t$, the web thickness, is replaced by $h$, the timber flange depth at the contact faces, and $Q$ is the first moment of area of the upper timber flange about the neutral axis.

For long-term loading

$$
\begin{aligned}
V &= 1125 \ N \\
Q &= 169 \times 47 \times [(350 \div 2) - (47 \div 2)] = 1.2034 \times 10^6 \ mm^3 \\
I &= 391.84 \times 10^6 \ mm^4 \\
h &= 2 \times 47 \ mm = 94 \ mm
\end{aligned}
$$

giving rolling shear

$$
\frac{1125 \ N \times 1.2034 \times 10^6 \ mm^4}{391.84 \times 10^6 \ mm^4 \times 94 \ mm} = 0.037 \ N/mm^2.
$$

Permissible long-term rolling shear $= 0.35 \ N/mm^2 \times 1.0(K38) \times 0.5(K37) = 0.175 \ N/mm^2$.

The applied rolling shear of $0.037 \ N/mm^2$ is less than the permissible rolling shear of $0.175 \ N/mm^2$, therefore satisfactory.

For net medium-term loading

$$
\begin{aligned}
V &= 2500 \ N \\
Q &= 1.2034 \times 10^6 \ mm^3 \\
I &= 395.21 \times 10^6 \ mm^4 \\
h &= 94 \ mm
\end{aligned}
$$

giving

$$
\frac{2500 \ N \times 1.2034 \times 10^6 \ mm^3}{395.21 \times 10^6 \ mm^4 \times 94 \ mm} = 0.081 \ N/mm^2
$$

The total medium-term rolling shear $= 0.037 \ N/mm^2 + 0.081 \ N/mm^2$

= 0.118 N/mm$^2$ which is less than the permissible medium-term rolling shear stress of 0.35 N/mm$^2$ × 1.50($K38$) × 0.5($K37$) = 0.263 N/mm$^2$, therefore satisfactory.

*Deflection*

The total permissible deflection due to bending and shear effects is limited to 0.003 × effective span (section 3.10 (clause 14.7)) = 0.003 × 5000 mm = 15 mm.

*Bending deflection*

The deflection due to bending is found by summing separately the deflection due to long-term loading and net medium-term loading using

$$\text{deflection} = \frac{5WL^3}{384EI}.$$

For long-term loading

$$
\begin{aligned}
W &= 2250 \text{ N} \\
L &= 5000 \text{ mm} \\
I &= 391.81 \times 10^6 \text{ mm}^4 \\
E &= 7000 \text{ N/mm}^2 \times 1.14(K28) = 7980 \text{ N/mm}^2
\end{aligned}
$$

giving deflection

$$\frac{5 \times 2250 \text{ N} \times (5000 \text{ mm})^3}{384 \times 391.81 \times 10^6 \text{ mm}^4 \times 7980 \text{ N/mm}^2} = 1.171 \text{ mm}.$$

For medium-term loading

$$
\begin{aligned}
W &= 5000 \text{ N} \\
L &= 5000 \text{ mm} \\
I &= 395.21 \times 10^6 \text{ mm}^4 \\
E &= 7980 \text{ N/mm}^2
\end{aligned}
$$

giving deflection

$$= \frac{5 \times 5000 \text{ N} \times (5000 \text{ mm})^3}{384 \times 395.21 \times 10^6 \text{ mm}^4 \times 7980 \text{ N/mm}^2} = 2.580 \text{ mm}.$$

Total bending deflection = 1.171 mm + 2.580 mm = 3.751 mm.

*Shear deflection*

The shear deflection is found from $WL/8Cbd$ where the shearing forces are found over the whole web area, $b$, $d$.

For long-term loading

$W$ = 2250 N
$L$ = 5000 mm
$b$ = 2 webs × 3.40 mm = 6.80 mm transformed section
$d$ = 256 mm
$C$ = shear modulus

$$= 550 \text{ N/mm}^2 \times \frac{E_{\text{timber}}}{E_{\text{hardboard}}} \times K39$$

$$= 550 \text{ N/mm}^2 \times \frac{7980 \text{ N/mm}^2}{3256 \text{ N/mm}^2} \times K39$$

where $K39$ = applied panel shear stress ÷ permissible panel shear stress

$$= \frac{0.257 \text{ N/mm}^2}{1.55 \text{ N/mm}^2} = 0.1658$$

which from Table 57 gives $K39 = 2.854$ giving

$$C = 550 \text{ N/mm}^2 \times \frac{7980 \text{ N/mm}^2}{3256 \text{ N/mm}^2} \times 2.854(K39) = 3847 \text{ N/mm}^2.$$

Long-term shear deflection

$$= \frac{2250 \text{ N} \times 5000 \text{ mm}}{8 \times 3847 \text{ N/mm}^2 \times 6.8 \text{ mm} \times 256 \text{ mm}} = 0.210 \text{ mm}.$$

For medium-term shear deflection

$W$ = 5000 N
$L$ = 5000 mm
$b$ = 2 × 3.872 mm = 7.744 mm
$d$ = 256 mm

$$C = \text{shear modulus} = 550 \text{ N/mm}^2 \times \frac{7980 \text{ N/mm}^2}{3713 \text{ N/mm}^2} \times K40$$

$$K40 = \frac{\text{applied net medium-term panel shear}}{\text{permissible medium-term panel shear}}$$

$$= \frac{0.573 \text{ N/mm}^2}{2.325 \text{ N/mm}^2} = 0.246$$

which from Table 57 gives a $K40$ value of 3.378.

$$C = 550 \text{ N/mm}^2 \times \frac{7980 \text{ N/mm}^2}{3713 \text{ N/mm}^2} \times 3.378(K40) = 3993 \text{ N/mm}^2.$$

Net medium-term deflection

$$= \frac{5000 \text{ N} \times 5000 \text{ mm}}{8 \times 3993 \text{ N/mm}^2 \times 7.744 \text{ mm} \times 256 \text{ mm}} = 0.395 \text{ mm}.$$

Total shear deflection = 0.210 mm + 0.395 mm = 0.605 mm.

The total bending and shear deflection of 3.751 mm + 0.605 mm = 4.356 mm is less than the permissible deflection of 15 mm, therefore satisfactory.

## Lateral stability

The lateral stability must be checked in accordance with section 3.13 (clause 14.10), using the thinnest transformed section:

$$I_{xx} \frac{BD^3}{12} - \frac{bd^3}{12} = \frac{175.8 \times 350^3}{12} - \frac{169 \times 256^3}{12} = 391.84 \times 10^6 \text{ mm}^3$$

$$I_{yy} = \frac{DB^3}{12} - \frac{db^3}{12} = \frac{350 \times 175.8^3}{12} - \frac{256 \times 169^3}{12} = 55.497 \times 10^6 \text{ mm}^3$$

giving ratio of $\dfrac{I_{xx}}{I_{yy}} = \dfrac{391.84 \times 10^6 \text{ mm}^4}{55.497 \times 10^6 \text{ mm}^4} = 7.06.$

The ratio of 7.06 is between 5 and 10. The ends of the beam must be held in position at the bottom flange at the supports.

## Bearing stress

Two bearings, one at each end of the beam, 50 mm long and 150 mm wide will be provided.

$$W = 7.25 \text{ kN} \div 2 = 3.625 \text{ kN}$$

$A = 50\ mm \times 150\ mm = 7500\ mm^2$

Compression stress perpendicular to the grain

$$\frac{W}{A} = \frac{3625\ N}{7500\ mm^2} = 0.483\ N/mm^2.$$

Permissible compression stress perpendicular to the grain $= 2.1\ N/mm^2$
$\times\ 1.25(K3) \times 1.33(K29) = 3.49\ N/mm^2$.

The applied stress of $0.483\ N/mm^2$ is less than the permissible compression stress perpendicular to the grain of $3.49\ N/mm^2$, therefore satisfactory.

Web stiffeners may be needed at all points of concentrated load and at the bearings.

## 3.27 Design example 8: A wood chipboard box-beam cat-walk

*The wood chipboard box-beam shown in Figure 3.10 is to be used as the main structural member of a cat-walk. The dead load includes the necessary load spreading timbers and totals 500 N per metre run of the beam. The effective span is 5 metres. If the flanges are of SS grade whitewood and the webs are of type C5 wood chipboard, check that the proposed design is satisfactory. The imposed loading is as shown in Figure 3.9, but with the 1.0 kN point loads increased to 2.7 kN. The service conditions are such that the 'dry' stress values always apply.*

*Loading*

The dead load is $0.50\ kN/m \times 5\ m$ span $= 2.50\ kN$

The imposed load for a cat-walk is a concentrated load of 1 kN at 1 m centres as shown in Figure 3.9.

The dead load bending moment $= \dfrac{WL}{8} = \dfrac{2.5\ kN \times 5\ m}{8} = 1.563\ kNm.$

The worst imposed load positioning is as shown in Figure 3.9, with the first 2.7 kN load starting 0.5 m from the left-hand support. By taking moments about the centre line, the maximum imposed load bending moment is 8.775 kNm.

The duration of load modification factor $K81$ for wood chipboard is 1.0 for long-term loading and 1.80 for medium-term loading (Table 2.1 (Table 91e)). When a value of $K81$ other than 1.0 is used, the design must be checked for all other conditions of loading.

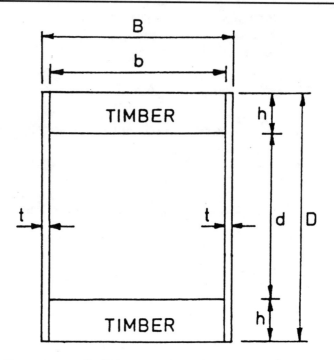

**Figure 3.10   Section through the wood chipboard box-beam**
B = 248 mm, b = 169 mm, h = 47 mm, D = 350 mm, d = 256 mm, t = 40 mm nominal, 39.5 mm minimum. Timber size  =  169 × 47 mm,  from  BS 5268: Pt 2, Table  99.  Sanded  chipboard  39.5 mm  minimum thickness.

The value of $K28$, to be applied to the minimum modulus of elasticity for deflection calculations, depends upon the total number of pieces of timber in both flanges, which is 2, giving $K28 = 1.14$. The modification factors $K27$, $K28$ and $K29$ are used as the box-beam must be designed as a built-up beam (section 3.13 (clause 14.10)).

The modulus of elasticity for the deflection calculations is the minimum  $E$  value  (Table  10)  of  7000 N/mm$^2$ × 1.14  ($K28$)  = 7980 N/mm$^2$.

As there will not be wane present in the whitewood flanges $K29 = 1.33$ (Table 26).

In the case of box-beams and any other composite beam, it is assumed that the materials are rigidly connected together and that the strain at the common surface will be the same. Each material has its own limiting stress and modulus of elasticity and it is necessary to determine which material is the limiting material:

$$\text{Strain} = \left(\frac{\text{stress}}{E}\right)_{\text{timber}} = \left(\frac{\text{stress}}{E}\right)_{\text{chipboard}}$$

*Timber*

The whitewood flanges are not being bent, but are resisting the load by compression and tension.

The permissible compression flange stress, for medium-term loading and for one piece of timber in the compression flange is:

7.9 N/mm$^2$ $\times$ $K3$ $\times$ $K28$ giving
7.9 N/mm$^2$ $\times$ 1.25 ($K3$) $\times$ 1.0 ($K28$) = 9.875 N/mm$^2$.

The permissible tension flange stress is:

4.5 N/mm$^2$ $\times$ $K3$ $\times$ $K14$ $\times$ $K27$, where $K14$ = width modification factor (section 5.6 (clause 16.2))

$$K14 = \left(\frac{300}{169}\right)^{0.11} = 1.0652$$

giving

4.5 N/mm$^2$ $\times$ 1.25($K3$) $\times$ 1.0652($K14$) $\times$ 1.0($K27$) = 5.992 N/mm$^2$.

The permissible tension stress of 5.992 N/mm$^2$ is less than the permissible compression stress of 9.875 N/mm$^2$, giving a limiting strain of:

$$\frac{5.992 \text{ N/mm}^2}{7000 \text{ N/mm}^2} = 855.9 \times 10^{-6}, \text{ using the minimum } E.$$

*Wood chipboard*

In the design of the box-beam, it is necessary to determine the correct chipboard modulus of elasticity, which varies according to the ratios applied to permissible stress for each load duration. To determine the correct value of the stress ratio, it may be necessary to carry out a series of iterative calculations. In the following calculation only the last iteration is shown.

For long-term loading assume a stress ratio of 0.10 (Table 91f) which gives $K82 = 5.17$. The long-term load $E$ value for tension (section 12.8 (clause 71)) $= 270 \text{ N/mm}^2 \times 5.17(K82) = 1396 \text{ N/mm}^2$.

The minimum timber $E$ value $= 7000 \text{ N/mm}^2$, giving a transformed wood chipboard thickness of

$$39.5 \text{ mm} \times \frac{1396 \text{ N/mm}^2}{7000 \text{ N/mm}^2} = 7.88 \text{ mm}.$$

Using the applied stress $My/I$ times the modular ratio, where

$M = 1.563$ kNm, the dead load bending moment,

$y = D \div 2 = 350 \div 2 = 175$ mm and

$I = \dfrac{BD^3}{12} - \dfrac{bd}{12}$ for the transformed section

$$= \left( \frac{[169 + (2 \times 7.88)] \times 350^3}{12} \right) = \left( \frac{169 \times 256^3}{12} \right)$$

$$= 660.132 \times 10^6 - 236.28 \times 10^6 = 423.85 \times 10^6 \text{ mm}^4$$

giving an applied stress of:

$$\frac{1.563 \times 10^6 \text{ Nmm} \times 175 \text{ mm}}{423.85 \times 10^6 \text{ mm}^4} \times \frac{1396 \text{ N/mm}^2}{7000 \text{ N/mm}^2} = 0.129 \text{ N/mm}^2.$$

The limiting permissible stress in the chipboard is the tensile stress of $1.31 \text{ N/mm}^2$ (Table 91c), which, when multiplied by the modification factor $K81$, gives a permissible long-term dead load stress of $1.31 \text{ N/mm}^2 \times 1.0 \ (K81) = 1.31 \text{ N/mm}^2$.

The applied stress to permissible stress ratio is:

$$\frac{0.129 \text{ N/mm}^2}{1.31 \text{ N/mm}^2} = 0.098 \simeq 0.10.$$

The chipboard strain is $\dfrac{0.129 \text{ N/mm}^2}{1396 \text{ N/mm}^2} = 92.41 \times 10^{-6}$

which is less than the maximum timber strain of $855.9 \times 10^{-6}$, therefore satisfactory.

For the net medium-term loads, a stress ratio of 0.3 is assumed, giving

$K83 = 5.02$ (Table 91f) and a medium-term $E$ value of $270$ N/mm$^2$ $\times$ $5.02(K40) = 1355$ N/mm$^2$. The transformed chipboard thickness is

$$39.5 \text{ mm} \times \frac{1355 \text{ N/mm}^2}{7000 \text{ N/mm}^2} = 7.65 \text{ mm}.$$

For the net medium-term loads, which refer to the loads of the duration stated and excludes all other loads of longer or shorter duration, we have

$$M = 8.775 \text{ kNm}$$
$$y = 175 \text{ mm}$$
$$I = \frac{[169 + (2 \times 7.65)] \times 350^3}{12} - \frac{169 \times 256^3}{12} = 422.21 \times 10^6 \text{ mm}^4$$

giving an applied stress of

$$\frac{8.775 \times 10^6 \text{ Nmm} \times 175 \text{ mm}}{422.21 \times 10^6 \text{ mm}^4} \times \frac{1355 \text{ N/mm}^2}{7000 \text{ N/mm}^2} = 0.704 \text{ N/mm}^2.$$

The limiting permissible tensile stress is $1.31$ N/mm$^2$ $\times$ $1.80(K81) = 2.358$ N/mm$^2$, giving a net medium-term stress ratio of

$$\frac{0.704}{2.358} = 0.299.$$

The chipboard strain is $\dfrac{0.704 \text{ N/mm}^2}{1355 \text{ N/mm}^2} = 519.56 \times 10^{-6}$

which is less than the maximum timber strain of $855.9 \times 10^6$, therefore satisfactory.

The total chipboard strain of $(519.56 + 92.41) \times 10^{-6} = 611.97 \times 10^{-6}$ is less than the maximum timber strain and is therefore satisfactory.

*Panel shear*

The panel shear in the chipboard must be checked for both long-term and net medium-term loadings using

$$\text{panel shear stress} = \frac{VQ}{tI_{xx}}$$

where $V = $ shear force, $Q = $ first moment of area of the section above and neutral axis, $I = $ second moment of area of the transformed section and $t$ = untransformed web thickness.

For long-term loading

$$V = 2.50 \text{ kN} \div 2 = 1250 \text{ N}$$

$$Q = 169 \times 47 \left(\frac{350}{2} - \frac{47}{2}\right) \text{ for the timber plus}$$

$$\left(2 \times 7.88 \times \frac{350}{2} \times \frac{350}{4}\right) \text{ for the chipboard}$$

$$= (1.2034 \times 10^6) + (0.2413 \times 10^6) = 1.4447 \times 10^6 \text{ mm}^3$$
$$I = 423.85 \times 10^6 \text{ mm}^4$$
$$t = 2 \times 39.5 \text{ mm} = 79 \text{ mm}$$

giving a panel shear stress of

$$\frac{1250 \text{ N} \times 1.4447 \times 10^6 \text{ mm}^3}{423.85 \times 10^6 \text{ mm}^4 \times 79 \text{ mm}} = 0.0539 \text{ N/mm}^2.$$

Allowable panel shear = $2.20 \text{ N/m}^2 \times 1.0(K81) = 2.20 \text{ N/mm}^2$.
   The long-term panel shear of $0.0539 \text{ N/mm}^2$ is less than the permissible panel shear of $2.20 \text{ N/mm}^2$, therefore satisfactory.
   For net medium-term loading:

$$V = (2.7 \text{ kN} \times 5 \div 2) = 6750 \text{ N}$$

$$Q = \left[169 \times 47 \left(\frac{350}{2} - \frac{47}{2}\right)\right] + \left[2 \times 7.65 \times \frac{350}{2} \times \frac{350}{4}\right]$$

$$= (1.2034 \times 10^6) + (0.2343 \times 10^6) = 1.4377 \times 10^6 \text{ mm}^3$$
$$I = 422.21 \times 10^6 \text{ mm}^4$$
$$t = 2 \times 39.5 = 79 \text{ mm}$$

giving a panel shear of

$$\frac{6750 \text{ N} \times 1.4377 \times 10^6 \text{ mm}^3}{422.21 \times 10^6 \text{ mm}^4 \times 79 \text{ mm}} = 0.291 \text{ N/mm}^2.$$

The permissible panel shear = $2.20 \text{ N/mm}^2 \times 1.80 \ (K81) = 3.96 \text{ N/mm}^2$.
   The net medium-term panel shear of $0.291 \text{ N/mm}^2$ plus the long-term panel shear of $0.0539 \text{ N/mm}^2$ totals $0.345 \text{ N/mm}^2$ and is less than the permissible panel shear of $3.96 \text{ N/mm}^2$, therefore satisfactory.

*Rolling shear*

Only the area of contact between the chipboard and the timber flange members can be considered in calculating rolling shear. A stress modification factor $K37 = 0.5$ must be applied to the grade rolling shear stress (clause 71).

The calculation for rolling shear uses the same equation as panel shear, except that $t$, the web thickness, is replaced by $h$, the timber flange depth at the contact faces, and $Q$ is the first moment of area of the upper timber flange about the neutral axis.

For long-term loading

$$V = 1250 \text{ N}$$

$$Q = 169 \times 47 \times \left(\frac{350}{2} - \frac{47}{2}\right) = 1.2034 \times 10^6 \text{ mm}^3$$

$$I = 423.85 \times 10^6 \text{ mm}^4$$
$$h = 2 \times 47 \text{ mm} = 94 \text{ mm}$$

giving rolling shear of

$$\frac{1250 \text{ N} \times 1.2034 \times 10^6 \text{ mm}^3}{423.85 \times 10^6 \text{ mm}^4 \times 94 \text{ mm}} = 0.038 \text{ N/mm}^2.$$

Permissible long-term rolling shear $= 0.42 \text{ N/mm}^2 \times 1.0(K81) \times 0.5$ $(K37) = 0.21 \text{ N/mm}^2$

The applied long-term rolling shear of $0.038 \text{ N/mm}^2$ is less than the long-term permissible shear of $0.21 \text{ N/mm}^2$, therefore satisfactory.

For net medium-term loading:

$$V = 6750 \text{ N}$$
$$Q = 1.2034 \times 10^6 \text{ mm}^3$$
$$I = 422.21 \times 10^6 \text{ mm}^4$$
$$h = 94 \text{ mm}$$

giving

$$\frac{6750 \text{ N} \times 1.2034 \times 10^6 \text{ mm}^3}{422.21 \times 10^6 \text{ mm}^4 \times 94 \text{ mm}} = 0.205 \text{ N/mm}^2.$$

The permissible medium-term rolling shear stress of $0.42 \text{ N/mm}^2 \times 1.80$ $(K81) \times 0.5(K37) = 0.378 \text{ N/mm}^2$ is larger than the total applied rolling shear of $0.038 \text{ N/mm}^2 + 0.205 \text{ N/mm}^2 = 0.243 \text{ N/mm}^2$, therefore satisfactory.

## Deflection

The total permissible deflection due to bending and shear effects is limited to $0.003 \times$ effective span (section 3.10 (clause 14.7)) $= 0.003 \times$ 5 m $= 15$ mm.

*Bending deflection*  The deflection due to bending is found by summing separately the deflection due to long-term loading and the deflection due to net medium-term loading.

The bending deflection $= \dfrac{5WL^3}{384EI}$.

For long-term loading

$W = 2500$ N
$I = 423.85 \times 10^6$ mm
$L = 5000$ mm
$E = 7000$ N/mm$^2 \times 1.14(K28) = 7980$ N/mm$^2$

giving a deflection of

$$\frac{5 \times 2500 \text{ N} \times (5000 \text{ mm})^3}{384 \times 423.85 \times 10^6 \text{ mm}^4 \times 7980 \text{ N/mm}^2} = 1.203 \text{ mm}.$$

For the medium-term load

$W = 13\ 500$ N
$L = 5000$ mm
$I = 422.21 \times 10^6$ mm$^4$
$E = 7980$ N/mm$^2$

giving a deflection of

$$\frac{5 \times 13\ 500 \text{ N} \times (5000 \text{ mm})^3}{384 \times 422.21 \times 10^6 \text{ mm}^4 \times 7980 \text{ N/mm}^2} = 6.522 \text{ mm}.$$

Total bending deflection $= 1.203$ mm $+ 6.522$ mm $= 7.725$ mm

*Shear deflection*  The shear deflection is found from $WL/8Cbd$, where the shear forces are found over the whole web area, $b$, $d$.
   For long-term loading:

$W = 2500$ N
$L = 5000$ mm
$b = 2$ webs $\times 7.88$ mm $= 15.76$ mm transformed section
$d = 256$ mm
$C = $ shear modulus

$$= 200 \text{ N/mm}^2 \times \left(\frac{E_{\text{timber}}}{E_{\text{chipboard}}}\right) \times K82$$

$$= 200 \text{ N/mm}^2 \times \left(\frac{7980 \text{ N/mm}^2}{1396 \text{ N/mm}^2}\right) \times K82$$

where $K82 = \dfrac{\text{applied panel shear stress}}{\text{permissible panel shear stress}}$

$$= \frac{0.0539 \text{ N/mm}^2}{2.20 \text{ N/mm}^2} = 0.0245$$

which from Table 91f gives $K82 = 5.517$, giving

$$C = 200 \text{ N/mm}^2 \times \left(\frac{7980 \text{ N/mm}^2}{1396 \text{ N/mm}^2}\right) \times 5.517(K82) = 6307 \text{ N/mm}^2.$$

Long-term shear deflection

$$= \frac{2500 \text{ N} \times 5000 \text{ mm}}{8 \times 6307 \text{ N/mm}^2 \times 15.76 \text{ mm} \times 256 \text{ mm}} = 0.061 \text{ mm}.$$

For medium-term shear deflection

$$
\begin{aligned}
W &= 6750 \text{ N} \\
L &= 5000 \text{ mm} \\
b &= 2 \times 7.65 \text{ mm} = 15.3 \text{ mm} \\
d &= 256 \text{ mm} \\
C &= \text{shear modulus} = 200 \text{ N/mm}^2 \times \frac{7980 \text{ N/mm}^2}{1355 \text{ N/mm}^2} \times K83
\end{aligned}
$$

where $K83 = \dfrac{\text{applied net medium-term panel shear}}{\text{permissible medium-term panel shear}}$

$$= \frac{0.291 \text{ N/mm}^2}{3.96 \text{ N/mm}^2} = 0.0735$$

which from Table 91f gives a $K83$ value of 5.483

$$C = 200 \text{ N/mm}^2 \times \left(\frac{7980 \text{ N/mm}^2}{1355 \text{ N/mm}^2}\right) \times 5.483(K83) = 6458 \text{ N/mm}^2.$$

Net medium-term deflection

$$= \frac{13\,500 \text{ N} \times 5000 \text{ mm}}{8 \times 6458 \text{ N/mm}^2 \times 15.3 \text{ mm} \times 256 \text{ mm}} = 0.333 \text{ mm}.$$

**79**

Total shear deflection $= 0.061$ mm $+ 0.333$ mm $= 0.394$ mm.

The total bending and shear deflection of 7.725 mm $+ 0.394$ mm $=$ 8.12 mm is less than the permissible deflection of 15 mm, therefore satisfactory.

*Lateral stability*

The lateral stability must be checked in accordance with section 3.13 (clause 14.10), using the thinnest transformed section.

$$B = (169 + 7.65 + 7.65) = 184.3 \text{ mm}$$

$$I_{xx} = \frac{BD^3}{12} - \frac{bd}{12}$$

$$= \frac{184.3 \text{ mm} \times (350 \text{ mm})^3}{12} - \frac{169 \text{ mm} \times (256 \text{ mm})^3}{12}$$

$$= 422.21 \times 10^6 \text{ mm}^4$$

$$I_{yy} = \frac{DB^3}{12} - \frac{db^3}{12}$$

$$= \frac{350 \text{ mm} \times (184.3 \text{ mm})^3}{12} - \frac{256 \text{ mm} \times (169 \text{ mm})^3}{12}$$

$$= 79.61 \times 10^6 \text{ mm}^4$$

giving a ratio of $\dfrac{I_{xx}}{I_{yy}} = \dfrac{422.21 \times 10^6 \text{ mm}^4}{79.61 \times 10^6 \text{ mm}^4} = 5.303.$

The ratio of 5.303 is between 5 and 10. The ends of the beam should be held in position at the bottom flange at the supports.

*Bearing stress*

Two bearings, one at each end of the beam, 50 mm long and 150 mm wide, will be provided.

$$W = \frac{2.5 \text{ kN} + 13.5 \text{ kN}}{2} = 8 \text{ kN}$$

$$A = 50 \text{ mm} \times 150 \text{ mm} = 7500 \text{ mm}^2$$

Compression perpendicular to the grain $= \dfrac{W}{A} = \dfrac{8000 \text{ N}}{7500 \text{ mm}} = 1.07 \text{ N/mm}^2.$

Permissible timber compressive stress perpendicular to the grain is

$2.1 \text{ N/mm}^2 \times 1.24(K3) \times 1.33(K29) = 3.49 \text{ N/mm}^2$.

The applied stress of $1.07 \text{ N/mm}^2$ is less than the permissible compressive stress perpendicular to the grain of $3.49 \text{ N/mm}^2$, therefore satisfactory.

Web stiffness may be needed at all points of concentrated load and at the bearings.

# 4 Compression members

## 4.1 Introduction

In the design of compression members the permissible stresses in the direction of the grain are governed in the usual way by the particular conditions of service, loading (BS 5268: Pt 2, clause 12), exposure condition (clause 10.2), load sharing (clause 13), the limiting of bow to 1/300th of the column length and the additional factors given in this chapter. The limitation on bow (clause 15.1) is required as the stress grading rules are inadequate for the selection of materials for columns, where straightness is particularly important.

## 4.2 Timber size factors

The grade compression stresses given in BS 5268: Pt 2, Tables 9, 10 and 15 are to be used for all solid timber and laminations graded in accordance with BS 4978 or BS 5756. For solid timber graded to North American NLGA or NGRDL rules and not assigned to a strength class the grade compressive stress of Tables 11 and 12 in BS 5268: Pt 2 are multiplied by the factor $K10$ appropriate to the cross-sectional size given in Table 14 of Part 2. The modulus of elasticity is also multiplied by a modification factor $K11$ of Table 14 when making buckling calculations. The factors $K10$ and $K11$ have a value of 1.0 for North American grades and sizes not listed in Table 14 and for structural light framing, light framing and stud 38 × 89 mm and all joist and plank grades and sizes.

## 4.3 Effective length

The effective length of the compression member can be found by using either Table 4.1 or from the distance between the adjacent points of zero bending between which the member is in single curvature.

**Table 4.1  Effective length of compression members**

| End conditions | Effective length ($L_e$) Actual length (L) |
|---|---|
| Restrained at both ends in position and in direction | 0.7 |
| Restrained at both ends in position and at one end in direction | 0.85 |
| Restrained at both ends in position but not in direction | 1.0 |
| Restrained at one end in position and in direction and at the other end in direction but not in position | 1.5 |
| Restrained at one end in position and in direction and free at the other end | 2.0 |

Source: Reproduced with permission from BS 5268: Pt 2

## 4.4 Slenderness ratio

The slenderness ratio of the compression member is found by dividing the effective length $L_e$ by the radius of gyration, $i$. The slenderness ratio should not exceed 180 if the compression member is carrying dead and imposed load other than wind loads or where the compression member's deflection will adversely affect the stress in another member carrying dead and imposed loads other than wind loads.

A slenderness ratio of up to 250 is allowed for any member normally subjected to tension or combined tension and bending arising from dead and imposed loads, but subjected to a reversal of axial stress solely from the effects of wind and for any compression member carrying self weight and wind loads only, for example in the case of wind bracing.

## 4.5 Axial compression

If the slenderness ratio of the compression member is less than 5 and there is little eccentricity of loading, the permissible stress is the grade compression stress parallel to the grain modified as appropriate for member size (section 4.2 (BS 5268: Pt 2, clause 15.2)), moisture content (clause 10), duration of load (clause 12) and load sharing (clause 13) in the usual way.

For members with a slenderness ratio equal to, or more than, 5 the permissible stress is additionally modified by the factor $K12$ given in BS 5268: Pt 2, Table 22. The value of $K12$ can also be calculated using the equation given in Appendix C of BS 5268: Pt 2. When using Table 22 or Appendix C the value of the compression parallel to the grain is the grade stress modified only for moisture content, load duration and member size.

The minimum modulus of elasticity is needed for Table 22 or Appendix C for both load-sharing and non load-sharing compression members. If two or more pieces of timber are used to form a single compressive member, the minimum modulus of elasticity is further increased by $K9$ (Table 3.4 above), the modification factor for trimmer joists and lintels, or $K28$, the modification factor for vertically-glued laminated members. For members that are horizontally-glued laminated, the modified mean modulus of elasticity is used as described in section 6.2 (BS 5268: Pt 2, clause 18) and sections 4.12 and 6.7 (BS 5268: Pt 2, clause 22).

It is necessary to check each loading case to ensure the relevant permissible compressive stress is not exceeded. The value of compressive stress required when using Table 22 or Appendix C is modified for load duration for each load case.

## 4.6 Axial compression and bending

The size of a compression member subjected to bending and compression should be such that it will restrict the deflection to within the limits appropriate to the type of structure.

The effective length is the distance between the adjacent points of zero bending between which the member is in single curvature (section 4.3 (BS 5268: Pt 2, clause 15.3(b))). It is assumed that the member is restrained at both ends, in position but not in direction, otherwise the formula given below cannot be used.

If the member is part of a load-sharing system, the permissible bending stress $\sigma_{m,adm,\parallel}$ and the permissible compression stress $\sigma_{c,adm,\parallel}$

which includes $K12$ must be multiplied by the load-sharing modification factor $K8 = 1.1$, or $K27$ or $K28$, the modification factors for vertically-glued laminated members, as appropriate.

The bending and compression stresses must be so arranged that:

$$\frac{\sigma_{m,a,\parallel}}{\sigma_{m,adm,\parallel}\left(1 - \frac{1.5\sigma_{c,a,\parallel}}{\sigma_e} \times K12\right)} + \frac{\sigma_{c,a,\parallel}}{\sigma_{c,adm,\parallel}} \leq 1 \qquad (4.1)$$

where $\sigma_{m,a,\parallel}$ is the applied bending stress, $\sigma_{c,a,\parallel}$ is the applied compressive stress, and $\sigma_e$ is the Euler critical stress $\pi^2 E/(L_e/i)^2$ using the modulus of elasticity as described in section 4.5 (BS 5268: Pt 2, clause 15.5).

## 4.7 Notching and drilling

Allowances must be made in the design of a compression member for any notches or holes that are made. If circular holes in the member have diameters not greater than 25 per cent of the member width and are located on the neutral axis between 25 and 40 per cent of the actual length from an end or a support, then their effect need not be calculated.

## 4.8 Spaced columns

A spaced column is defined as two or more equal shafts, spaced apart at their ends and at intermediate points by packing blocks. The clear space between the shafts must not be greater than three times the shaft thickness, measured in the same plane. The packing blocks may be glued, bolted, screwed, nailed or connected in position in accordance with the next section (BS 5268: Pt 2, clause 15.9 and Section 6).

## 4.9 Packs for spaced columns

End packs that are mechanically connected should have sufficient length to accommodate the nails, screws or connectors that are required to transmit, between the abutting face of the packing and one adjacent shaft, a shear force equal to:

$$\frac{1.3Ab\sigma_{c,a,\parallel}}{na} \qquad (4.2)$$

where $A$ is the total cross-sectional area of the column, $b$ is the breadth of

**85**

the shaft, $\sigma_{c,a,\parallel}$ is the applied compressive stress, $n$ is the number of shafts, and $a$ is the distance between the centres of adjacent shafts.

The length of the packing measured along the axis of the column must not be less than six times the thickness of the individual shaft.

End packs that are glued must be of sufficient length to provide a glued area between the abutting face of the packing and one adjacent shaft that will transmit the same shearing force as for a mechanical connection. The minimum length requirement is also the same.

Intermediate packs must be at least 230 mm long along the column axis and be designed to transmit a shearing force of not less than half of the shearing force for the end packs. If the column length does not exceed 30 times the shaft thickness, then only one intermediate packing is required. The greatest slenderness ratio of the local portion of an individual shaft between packings is, however, limited to either 70, or 0.7 times the slenderness ratio of the whole column, whichever is the lesser. The effective length of the local portion of an individual shaft is the length between the centroids of the group of adjacent packings.

## 4.10 Permissible stresses for spaced columns

Figure 4.1 shows the relevant X–X and Y–Y axes for a spaced column. The permissible load is the least of the following:

1  that of a solid column, with the same cross-sectional area, bending about the X–X axis;
2  that of a solid column whose area is that of one member of the built-up column, with an effective length equal to the spacing of the packing pieces, multiplied by the number of shafts; or,
3  that of a column bending about the Y–Y axis with the same geometrical properties of cross-section as the built-up column, but with the effective length multiplied by the modification factor $K13$ as given in Table 23 of BS 5268: Pt 2.

## 4.11 Compression members in triangulated frames

In addition to the requirements of sections 4.1 to 4.10, compression members in triangulated frameworks, other than trussed rafters designed to BS 5268: Pt 3, are subject to the following requirements:

1  For continuous compression members, the effective length is taken as between 0.85 and 1.0 times the distance between the framework

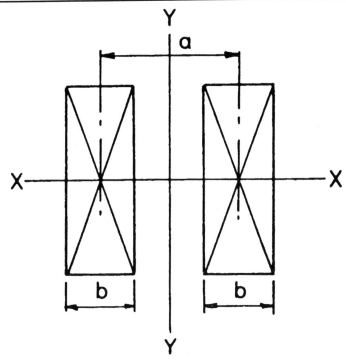

**Figure 4.1  Axes for a spaced column**

node points for buckling in the plane of the framework; or the actual distance between the effective lateral restraint for buckling perpendicular to the plane of the framework. The value of between 0.85 and 1.0 to be used is dependent upon the degree of fixity and the distribution of load between the node points.

2  For non-continuous compression members, such as web members in a framework, the effective length of buckling depends upon the type of end connection described in Table 4.1. If the compression member only has one bolt or connector that permits rotation at the end of the member then the effective length is the actual length. For web members fastened by gusset plates which partially restrain the member at both ends in position and direction, the effective length for buckling in and out of the plane of the truss is 0.9 times the actual distance between the points of intersection of the lines passing through the centroids of the members connected.

3  For spaced compression members in triangulated frameworks, section 4.9 (BS 5268: Pt 2, clauses 15.9.1.1 and 15.9.2) does not apply. Intermediate packing should not be less than 200 mm long and fixed in such a manner as to transmit a tensile force parallel to

the X–X axis, between the individual members, of not less than 2.5 per cent of the total axial force in the spaced compression members.

## 4.12  Glued laminated compression members

This chapter applies to glued laminated timber compression members, but the mean modulus of elasticity is used in accordance with the grade stresses for horizontally-glued laminated members (section 6.2 (BS 5268: Pt 2, clause 18)) to calculate the value of $K12$ in Table 22. Care must be exercised in determining whether the laminations are parallel to the neutral plane (horizontally-glued laminated), in which case clause 18 applies, or whether the laminations are at right angles to the neutral plane (vertically-glued laminated), in which case clause 19 applies.

## 4.13  Design example 1: Axially and wind-loaded solid timber column

*A solid timber column of SC4 is 4 metres long. It is restrained at both ends in position and at one end, the base, in direction. If the medium-term applied dead and temporary imposed axial load is 35 kN and the very short-term imposed wind load, applied to the major axis, is 5 kN/m, determine whether the chosen sawn softwood section size of 200 × 150 mm is adequate.*

For a softwood of SC4, the long-term grade stresses are found in BS 5268: Pt 2, Table 9 and are as follows:

Bending parallel to the grain       =  7.5 N/mm$^2$
Compression parallel to the grain  =  7.9 N/mm$^2$
Minimum modulus of elasticity     =  6600 N/mm$^2$

The medium-term load modification factor $K3$ is 1.25, while for the very short-term loading $K3 = 1.75$ (Table 2.1).

The column is an internal column and the dry exposure condition applies (section 5.3 (BS 5268: Pt 2, clause 10.1)).

The column is non-load-sharing (section 2.8 (BS 5268: Pt 2, clause 13)) and $K8 = 1.0$.

The column must also be checked to ensure that the bow is less than the grade limit of 1/300th of the length.

The softwood is graded in accordance with BS 4978 and assigned to a strength class, consequently the size factor does not apply (section 4.2).

The effective length $(L_e)$ of the column is found from Table 4.1 which for the given end conditions is $L_e = 0.85 \times 4000$ mm $= 3400$ mm.

The slenderness ratio $(\lambda)$ is the effective length divided by the radius of gyration $(i)$. For dead and imposed loads, the slenderness ratio must be less than 180. Using Table 98 (BS 5268: Pt 2) the radius of gyration about the X–X axis is 57.7 mm and about the Y–Y axis is 43.3 mm. Taking the minimum value of $i$, the slenderness ratio is 3400 mm/43.3 mm $= 78.52$ which is less than 180.

For the wind loading, which is applied to the X–X axis, the slenderness ratio is 3400 mm/57.7 mm $= 58.93$ which is less than 250.

For axial compression only and with a slenderness ratio greater than 5, the minimum modulus of elasticity is used for entry to Table 22 (BS 5268: Pt 2). The permissible stress is the grade compressive stress parallel to the grain multiplied by the duration of load factor $K3$:

7.9 N/mm$^2$ $\times$ 1.25$(K3) = 9.875$ N/mm$^2$.

For entry into Table 22:

$$E\text{min}/9.875 \text{ N/mm}^2 = \frac{6600 \text{ N/mm}^2}{9.875 \text{ N/mm}^2} = 668,$$

and the slenderness ratio is 78.52, which gives a value of $K12 = 0.467$.

The permissible compressive stress is

9.875 N/mm$^2$ $\times$ 0.467$(K12) = 4.61$ N/mm$^2$.

The applied compressive stress is

$$\frac{35\,000 \text{ N}}{200 \text{ mm} \times 150 \text{ mm}} = 1.167 \text{ N/mm}^2.$$

The applied compressive stress of 1.167 N/mm$^2$ is less than the permissible compressive stress of 4.62 N/mm$^2$. The column is satisfactory for the applied axial loading.

Looking at the imposed wind load of 5 kN/m (equivalent to a UDL of 10 N over the 4 m length of the column on the major axis, section 4.6 (BS 5268: Pt 2, clause 15.6) applies. The bending stress is found from $My/I$ where $M = 5 \times 10^6$ Nmm and $I/y$ about the X–X axis is $1000 \times 10^3$ mm$^3$ (BS 5268: Pt 2, Table 98) giving a stress of $5 \times 10^6$ Nmm/$1000 \times 10^3$ mm$^3 = 5.0$ N/mm$^2$.

The permissible bending stress is the grade bending stress parallel to the grain (7.5 N/mm$^2$) multiplied by $K3$ the load duration factor for very short-term loading (1.75) multiplied by the depth factor $K7$ (section 3.9 (BS 5268: Pt 2, clause 14.6)).

$K7 = (300/200)^{0.11} = 1.0456$ giving a permissible bending stress of $7.5\ \text{N/mm}^2 \times 1.75(K3) \times 1.0456(K7) = 13.724\ \text{N/mm}^2$.

The applied compressive stress is $1.167\ \text{N/mm}^2$ and the permissible compressive stress is

$$7.9\ \text{N/mm}^2 \times 1.75(K3) \times K12 = 13.825 \times K12\ \text{N/mm}^2.$$

For entry into Table 22 the value of

$$\frac{E\text{min}}{13.825\ \text{N/mm}^2} = \frac{6600\ \text{N/mm}^2}{13.825\ \text{N/mm}^2} = 477,$$

and the slenderness ratio $\lambda = 58.93$, giving $K12 = 0.560$ and a permissible compressive stress of

$$13.825\ \text{N/mm}^2 \times 0.560(K12) = 7.75\ \text{N/mm}^2.$$

It is also necessary in using Equation 4.1 (BS 5268: Pt 2, clause 15.6) for the Euler critical stress $\sigma_e$ to be found as follows:

$$\sigma_e = \frac{\pi^2\ E\text{min}}{\left(\frac{L_e}{i}\right)^2}$$

where $E\text{min} = 6600\ \text{N/mm}^2$

and $\frac{L_e}{i} = 58.93$

giving

$$\sigma_e = \frac{\pi^2 6600\ \text{N/mm}^2}{58.93^2} = 18.76\ \text{N/mm}^2.$$

Substituting the values into Equation 4.1 gives

$$\frac{5.0\ \text{N/mm}^2}{13.724\ \text{N/mm}^2\left(1 - \dfrac{1.5 \times 1.167\ \text{N/mm}^2}{18.76\ \text{N/mm}^2} \times 0.56\right)} + \frac{1.167\ \text{N/mm}^2}{7.75\ \text{N/mm}^2}$$

$$= 0.384 + 0.151 = 0.535 \leqslant 1,$$

therefore satisfactory.

The column bow is limited to the grade limit of length divided by 300 which is 4000 mm ÷ 300 = 13.33 mm. The actual bow is found by considering the column as a beam subjected to a UDL due to the wind loading.

$$\text{Deflection} = \frac{5 \times WL^3}{384 \times E \times I}$$

where $W = 10\ 000$ N, $L = 4000$ mm, $E = 6600$ N/mm$^2$ and $I = 100 \times 10^6$ mm$^4$ giving a deflection of 12.63 mm which is less than the permissible bow of 13.33 mm.

The column should also be checked for the long-term loading condition.

## 4.14 Design example 2: Axially-loaded glued laminated timber column

*An LB grade glued laminated internal timber column, with an effective length of 5000 mm is subjected to a medium-term load of 600 kN. If 16 No. 45 mm-thick, SS grade whitewood laminations, 185 mm wide are to be used, determine if the section size is satisfactory.*

For SS grade whitewood (BS 5268: Pt 2, Table 9):

Compression parallel to the grain = 7.9 N/mm$^2$
Mean modulus of elasticity = 10 500 N/mm$^2$
Minimum modulus of elasticity = 7000 N/mm$^2$

The column is an internal column and the dry exposure condition applies (section 5.3 (BS 5268: Pt 2, clause 10.1)).

The column is non-load-sharing (section 2.8 (clause 13)) and $K8 = 0$.

The loading is medium-term and $K3 = 1.25$.

The column is horizontally glued such that the laminations are parallel to the neutral axis. The permissible stresses are governed by the modification factors $K15$ to $K20$ of Table 24 (BS 5268: Pt 2), that are appropriate to 16 No. laminations.

$K15 = 1.48$ Bending parallel to the grain
$K16 = 1.48$ Tension parallel to the grain
$K17 = 1.04$ Compression parallel to the grain
$K18 = 1.33$ Compression perpendicular to the grain

$K19 = 2.0$  Shear parallel to the grain
$K20 = 1.05$ Modulus of elasticity.

Permissible compressive stress

$$= \text{SS grade stress} \times K3 \times K12 \times K17$$
$$= 7.9 \text{ N/mm}^2 \times 1.25(K3) \times 1.04(K17) \times K12$$
$$= 10.27 \times K12 \text{ N/mm}^2.$$

The size factor does not apply as the softwood is graded in accordance with BS 4978 and assigned to a strength class (section 4.2 (BS 5268: Pt 2, clause 15.2)).

The slenderness ratio ($\lambda$) is the effective length ($L_e$) of 5000 mm divided by the minimum radius of gyration ($i$). For a 185 $\times$ 720 mm section, the minimum $i$ value is 53.405, giving a slenderness ratio of

$$\frac{5000 \text{ mm}}{53.405 \text{ mm}} = 93.624.$$

The value of 93.624 is less than the maximum value of 180 allowed for a compression member carrying dead and imposed load (clause 15.4).

For axial compression members acting alone, with a slenderness ratio greater than 5, the minimum modulus of elasticity (7000 N/mm$^2$) is used (clause 15.5), but clause 22 states that for glued laminated compression members, the mean modulus of elasticity (10 500 N/mm$^2$) modified in accordance with clause 18 should be used. The correct value of $E$ for entry into Table 22 (BS 5268: Pt 2) is found as follows:

$$10\ 500 \text{ N/mm}^2 \times 1.05(K20) = 11\ 025 \text{ N/mm}^2.$$

For entry into Table 22, we require the value of the slenderness ratio $\lambda$ (93.624) and the modified mean modulus of elasticity (11 025 N/mm$^2$), divided by the grade compressive stress parallel to the grain (7.9 N/mm$^2$ modified for moisture content ($K2 = 1.0$ due to the dry exposure condition) and duration of loading ($K3 = 1.25$) giving

$$\frac{E}{\sigma_{c,\|}} = \frac{11\ 025 \text{ N/mm}^2}{7.9 \text{ N/mm}^2 \times 1.25(K3) \times 1.0(K2)} = 1116.46$$

Using the values of 93.624, 1116.46 and Table 20, $K12$ is found to be 0.479. The permissible compressive stress is

$$10.27 \text{ N/mm}^2 \times 0.479(K12) = 4.917 \text{ N/mm}^2.$$

The allowable compressive force

$= $ cross-sectional area $\times$ 4.917 N/mm$^2$ $=$ 185 mm $\times$ 720 mm $\times$ 4.917 N/mm$^2$ $=$ 654.94 kN.

The allowable compressive force of 654.94 is larger than the applied compressive force of 600 kN and is satisfactory.

# 5 Tension members

## 5.1 Introduction

The permissible stresses for tension members depend upon the exposure condition, the duration of loading, load sharing, width factor, axial tension and bending stresses.

## 5.2 Dry exposure stresses

The British Standard assumes that all solid timber will be used where its equilibrium moisture content will not exceed 18 per cent for any significant period and the stresses given in BS 5268: Pt 2, Tables 9, 10, 11, 12, 13 and 15 are the dry grade stresses. Table 5.1 opposite lists the titles of Tables 9 to 13 and 15.

## 5.3 Wet exposure stresses

If the solid timber is likely to have an equilibrium moisture condition exceeding 18 per cent for any significant period, the dry stresses must be multiplied by the wet exposure modification factor $K2$ as shown in Table 5.2.

**Table 5.1   List of dry stress tables (BS 5268: Pt 2)**

| Table no. | Table title |
| --- | --- |
| 9 | Grade stresses and moduli of elasticity for strength classes |
| 10 | Grade stresses for softwoods: graded to BS 4978 rules |
| 11 | Grade stresses for Canadian softwoods: graded to NLGA rules |
| 12 | Grade stresses for USA softwoods: graded to NGRDL rules |
| 13 | Grade stresses for North American softwoods, graded to North American MSR rules |
| 15 | Grade stresses for tropical hardwoods graded to BS 5756 rules |

**Table 5.2   Modification factor $K2$ used to obtain the wet stresses and moduli**

| Property | Value of $K2$ |
| --- | --- |
| Bending parallel to grain | 0.8 |
| Tension parallel to grain | 0.8 |
| Compression parallel to grain | 0.6 |
| Compression perpendicular to grain | 0.6 |
| Shear parallel to grain | 0.9 |
| Mean and minimum modulus of elasticity | 0.8 |

Source: Reproduced with permission from BS 5268: Pt 2

## 5.4   Duration of loading

The dry grade stresses of Tables 9 to 13 and 15 are for long-term loading and must be multiplied by the modification factor $K3$ of Table 2.1 for other load durations.

## 5.5   Load-sharing systems

If four or more members act as a load-sharing system as described in section 2.8, the appropriate grade stesses are multiplied by the load-sharing modification factor $K8$ which has a value of 1.1. The mean modulus of elasticity is used for calculating deflections and displacements under both dead and imposed loads.

## 5.6 Width factor

The grade tension stresses given in Tables 9, 10 and 15 are for solid timber with a width $h$ of 300 mm and for laminations graded in accordance with BS 4978 or BS 5756. The grade tension stresses given in Tables 11 and 12 are for solid timber graded to NLGA or NGRDL joist and plank, select structural, No. 1 and No. 2 grades having a width of 300 mm and, if graded to NLGA or NGRDL structural light framing, select structural No. 1 and No. 2 grades having a width of 89 mm. Table 13 of BS 5268: Pt 2 gives the tension stresses for North American softwoods, graded to North American MSR rules, and are for the particular width of timber quoted.

For other widths of solid timber in Tables 9, 10 and 15 graded to the joist and plank rules of Tables 10 and 11, the grade tension stress must be multiplied by the width modification factor $K14$ as follows:

1  For solid timber widths of 72 mm or less, $K14 = 1.17$.
2  If the solid timber or glue-laminated width is greater than 72 mm, $K14 = (300 \div h)^{0.11}$.

If other widths of solid timber are graded to North American structural light framing rules and are not assigned to a strength class, the modification factor $K14$ is as given in Table 14.

## 5.7 Timber not suitable for tension members

The light framing and stud grades structural light framing No. 3 and joist and plank No. 3 grades must not be used for tension members.

## 5.8 Members subjected to axial tension and bending

For members subjected to bending as well as axial tension, the relationship between the sums of the ratios of applied stress and permissible stresses as described in Equation 5.1 must not exceed 1.0.

$$\frac{\text{applied bending stress}}{\text{permissible bending stress}} + \frac{\text{applied tension stress}}{\text{permissible tension stress}} \leqslant 1 \qquad (5.1)$$

which may be written as follows:

$$\frac{\sigma_{m,a,\parallel}}{\sigma_{m,adm,\parallel}} + \frac{\sigma_{t,a,\parallel}}{\sigma_{t,adm,\parallel}} \leqslant 1 \qquad (5.2)$$

## 5.9 Design example 1: Axially-loaded solid timber tension member

*Imported SS grade parana pine of basic sawn size 63 × 200 mm is to be used to support an axial tensile load. Determine the permissible long-term load and the permissible medium-term load using the wet exposure condition.*

Imported SS grade parana pine, if graded to BS 4978, satisfies the requirements for SC4 (BS 5268: Pt 2, Tables 3 and 9), giving the grade tension parallel to the grain as 4.5 N/mm.

Cross-sectional area (Table 98) is $12.6 \times 10^3$ mm$^2$
Wet exposure condition (Table 5.2) is $K2 = 0.8$
Duration of loading (Table 2.1) is $K3 = 1.0$ long term
$K3 = 1.25$ medium term
Width factor $K14 = (300/200)^{0.11} = 1.0456$.

Long-term axial load:

$$4.5 \text{ N/mm}^2 \times 12.6 \times 10^3 \text{ mm}^2 \times 0.8(K2) \times 1.0(K3) \times 1.0456(K14) = 47.43 \text{ kN}. \tag{5.3}$$

Medium-term axial load:

$$4.5 \text{ N/mm}^2 \times 12.6 \times 10^3 \text{ mm}^2 \times 0.8(K2) \times 1.25(K3) \times 1.0456(K14) = 59.29 \text{ kN}. \tag{5.4}$$

Imported SS grade parana pine, although allocated to SC4, is also shown in Table 10 to have tension parallel to grain of 5.4 N/mm$^2$. This higher value could be used instead of the lower SC4 value in Equations 5.3 and 5.4 giving the following loads:

Long-term axial load     =  56.92 kN
Medium-term axial load  =  71.15 kN.

## 5.10 Design example 2: Axially-loaded tension member subjected to bending

*A SC4 solid timber member of basic size 63 × 200 mm is subjected to an axial force of 40 kN. Using the dry exposure stresses and a permissible very short-term bending stress of 13.2 N/mm$^2$, determine the maximum applied very short-term bending stress.*

SC4 grade tension parallel to the grain (Table 9) is 4.5 N/mm$^2$
Duration of loading (Table 2.1), very short-term is 1.75($K3$)
Width factor $K14 = (300/200)^{0.11} = 1.0456$

Permissible tension stress, $\sigma_{t,adm,\parallel}$

$$4.5 \text{ N/mm}^2 \text{ (Table 9)} \times 1.75(K3) \times 1.0456(K14) = 8.234 \text{ N/mm}^2. \quad (5.5)$$

Applied tension stress, $\sigma_{t,a,\parallel}$

$$40 \text{ kN} \div 12.6 \times 10^3 \text{ mm}^2 \text{ (Table 98)} = 3.175 \text{ N/mm}^2. \quad (5.6)$$

Permissible bending stress, $\sigma_{m,adm,\parallel}$

Given as 13.2 N/mm$^2$. $\quad (5.7)$

Applied bending stress, $\sigma_{m,a,\parallel}$:
Substituting the value of Equations 5.5, 5.6 and 5.7 into Equation 5.2 gives the following:

$$\frac{\sigma_{m,a,\parallel}}{13.2 \text{ N/mm}^2} + \frac{3.175 \text{ N/mm}^2}{8.234 \text{ N/mm}^2} \leq 1 \quad (5.8)$$

The maximum tensile value of $\sigma_{m,a,\parallel}$ is found to be 8.11 N/mm$^2$.

In bending, a tensile stress of 8.11 N/mm$^2$ will indicate an equal compressive stress on the opposite side of the neutral axis. This compressive stress must be added to the tension stress to ensure that the resulting stress does not exceed the permissible compressive stress parallel to the grain.

# 6 Glued laminated timber

## 6.1 Introduction

Glued laminated timber members must be manufactured in accordance with BS 4169. Softwoods must be stress graded to BS 4978 and hardwoods used for beams stress graded to BS 5756.

## 6.2 Grade stresses for horizontally-glued laminated members

The softwood grade stresses are the SS grade stresses for the species modified by the modification factors $K15$ to $K26$ (BS 5268: Pt 2, Tables 24 or 25) appropriate to the timber grades used for the laminations. Table 24 assumes only one grade of timber is used, while Table 25 applies when more than one grade of timber is used, such that not less than 25 per cent of the depth at both the top and bottom of the member is of the superior grade. For hardwood members, the HS grade stresses for the species should be multiplied by the LB grade modification factors $K15$ to $K20$ of Table 24. The member must have four or more laminations, all of similar thickness, for $K15$ to $K26$ to apply.

## 6.3 Glued end joints

For LB and LC laminations, the bending efficiency ratings of the end joints, regardless of the loading types, must be at least 70 and 55 per cent, respectively. If these efficiency ratings are not met, and for LA laminations in a horizontally-glued laminated softwood member, the maximum bending, tension or compression parallel to the grain stress to which a glued end joint in any one lamination is subjected should not exceed the following: the particular species SS grade stress, multiplied by the efficiency rating for the joint (given in BS 5268: Pt 2, Appendix F), multiplied by the appropriate modification factors for member size, moisture content, load duration and the appropriate modification factors $K30$, $K31$ or $K32$ from Table 27.

For horizontally-glued laminated hardwood members, the same modification process is applied as for the softwood LA laminations with the two exceptions that the SS grade stresses are replaced by the HS grade stresses and that the joint efficiency ratings must be determined by test.

In the case of vertically-glued laminated beams, the end joints must have an efficiency not less than that required for the strength class or timber species and grade as given in Appendix F and Table 88, unless the permissible stress is reduced accordingly.

Neither finger joints nor plain scarf joints in a lamination affect the modulus of elasticity, and the full-jointed lamination cross-section may be used for the strength and stiffness calculations. If other types of end joint are used their suitability should be established by test or the contribution of the lamination in which they occur should be omitted when calculating the section's strength and stiffness properties.

## 6.4  Glued laminated flexural members

The use of glued laminated timber allows the construction of large cross-section, long-span flexural members, limited in length only by transport requirements. Straight glued laminated flexural members are dealt with in sections 3.15 and 3.24.

## 6.5  Curved glued laminated beams

The permissible stresses are governed by the wet exposure stresses (section 5.3 and BS 5268: Pt 2, clause 10.2), duration of load (section 3.3 and clause 12), load-sharing systems (section 3.4 and clause 13), flexural members (Chapter 3 and clause 14) and the following considerations.

The member may be pre-cambered to offset the dead and permanently imposed loads and the deflection under live or intermittent loads must not exceed 0.003 times the span. Shear deflection must also be considered in addition to the bending deflection.

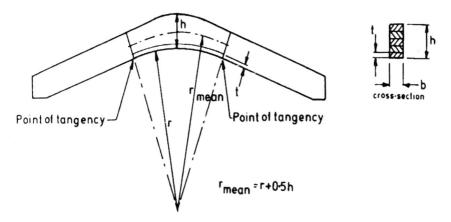

**Figure 6.1   Curved glued laminated beam**

If the cross-section of the beam is constant and rectangular as in Figure 6.1 the ratio of radius of curvature $r$, to the lamination thickness $t$, must be greater than 125 for softwoods and greater than 100 for hardwoods. If $r/t$ is less than 240, the bending tension and compression parallel to the grain grade stress must be multiplied by $K33$, where

$$K33 = 0.76 + 0.001 \,\frac{r}{t} \leq 1.0. \tag{6.1}$$

If $r_{mean}/h \leq 15$, then the extreme fibre bending stress $\sigma_m$ induced by the moment $M$ is found as follows:

For the concave face

$$\sigma_m = \frac{6M}{bh^2} \times K34 \tag{6.2}$$

where $K34 = 1 + \left(\dfrac{0.5h}{r_{mean}}\right)$ if $\dfrac{r_{mean}}{h} \leq 10$ $\qquad$ (6.3)

or $K34 = 1.15 \left(\dfrac{0.01\, r_{mean}}{h}\right)$ if $10 < \dfrac{r_{mean}}{h} \leq 15$. $\qquad$ (6.4)

For the convex face

$$\sigma_m = \frac{6M}{bh^2}. \tag{6.5}$$

The radial stress $\sigma_r$ due to $M$ must be calculated as follows:

$$\sigma_r = \frac{3M}{2bhr_{\text{mean}}}.$$ (6.6)

If $M$ increases $r_{\text{mean}}$, $\sigma_r$ will be tension perpendicular to the grain and must not exceed one third of the appropriate permissible shear stress parallel to the grain. If $M$ decreases $r_{\text{mean}}$, $\sigma_r$ will be in compression perpendicular to the grain and must not exceed 1.33 times the appropriate SS grade compression stress perpendicular to the grain for the species.

## 6.6 Pitched cambered softwood beams of rectangular section

For pitched cambered beams, as shown in Figure 6.2, and loaded symmetrically about the mid span, the apex bending stress is at a maximum at the soffit and is found from Equation 6.7:

$$\text{Apex bending stress} = \left(1 + \frac{(2.7 \times \tan \alpha)}{bh_{\text{apex}}^2}\right) \times 6M_{\text{apex}}$$ (6.7)

where $\alpha$ = the slope of the upper surface of the beam, $M_{\text{apex}}$ = apex bending moment, and $h_{\text{apex}}$ = depth of apex section.

The bending stress at the point of tangency is found from Equation 6.8:

$$\text{Point of tangency bending stress} = \frac{6M_{\text{tang}}}{bh_{\text{tang}}^2}$$ (6.8)

where $M_{\text{tang}}$ = point of tangency bending moment and $h_{\text{tang}}$ = depth of section at the point of tangency.

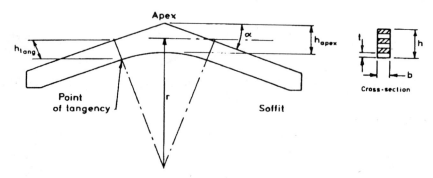

**Figure 6.2   Pitched cambered beam**

The stresses from Equations 6.7 and 6.8 must not exceed the appropriate permissible bending stress parallel to the grain.

The radial stress $\sigma_r$, perpendicular to the grain, induced by bending is at a maximum near the mid-depth at the apex, and is the larger of either Equation 6.9 or 6.10:

$$\sigma_r = \frac{6M_{\text{apex}}}{bh_{\text{apex}}^2} \times K35 \text{ or} \tag{6.9}$$

$$\sigma_r = \frac{3M_{\text{apex}}}{2rbh_{\text{apex}}} \tag{6.10}$$

where $r$, $b$ and $h_{\text{apex}}$ are as defined in Figure 6.2 and $K35$ is defined as follows:

$$K35 = A + \frac{Bh_{\text{apex}}}{r} + C\left(\frac{h_{\text{apex}}}{r}\right)^2. \tag{6.11}$$

The values of $A$, $B$ and $C$ are found from Table 28 and $\alpha$ is defined in Figure 6.2.

The tangent point radial stresses are found using Equation 6.6. The radial stresses at the tangent point and at the apex must not exceed one-third of the appropriate permissible stress in shear parallel to the grain.

## 6.7 Glued laminated compression members

Glued laminated compression members are dealt with in section 4.12.

## 6.8 Glued laminated tension members

Glued laminated tension members are subject to the provisions of sections 5.3–5.8.

## 6.9 Vertically-glued laminated beams

Vertically-glued laminated beams are dealt with in section 3.15.

## 6.10 Design example 1: Curved glued laminated roof beam

*A curved glued laminated roof beam, of constant cross-section, is to be manufactured from Redwood grade LB throughout. The beam has an effective span of 10 metres and a pitch of 20°. If the medium-term loading consists of a 2.5 kN/m dead load and an imposed load of 3 kN/m, determine the beam size and the amount of pre-camber.*

For SS grade Redwood the relevant grade stresses are:

Bending parallel to the grain  = 7.5 N/mm²
Shear parallel to the grain   = 0.82 N/mm²
Emean            = 10 500 N/mm²

Compression perpendicular to the grain = 2.1 N/mm².

The limiting live load deflection = 0.003 × effective span (section 6.5 (BS 5268: Pt 2, clause 21.2)) = 0.003 × 10 m = 30 mm.
The section size is determined from

$$\text{deflection} = \frac{5WL^3}{384EI} = 30 \text{ mm} \tag{6.12}$$

where $W = 3$ kN × 10 m = $30 × 10^3$ N imposed load, $L = 10\,000$ mm span, $E = 10\,500$ N/mm² × 1.05($K$20 from Table 24, LB grade) = 11 025 N/mm², and $I$ is to be determined.
Rearranging Equation 6.12 gives:

$$I = \frac{5 × 30 × 10^3 \text{ N} × (10\,000 \text{ mm})^3}{30 \text{ mm} × 384 × 11\,025 \text{ N/mm}^2} = 1.1810 × 10^9 \text{ mm}^4. \tag{6.13}$$

As the ends of the beam will be held in position, and due to the roof decking, the compression edge will be held in line, the maximum depth $d$, to breadth $b$, ratio will be 5 (section 3.11 (BS 5268: Pt 2, Table 19)).

As $I = \frac{bd^3}{12}$ and $\frac{d}{b} = 5$, then $I = \frac{d^4}{60}$ $\tag{6.14}$

giving $\frac{d^4}{60} = 1.1810 × 10^9$ mm⁴, with $d = 515.94$ mm and $b = 103.19$ mm.

The minimum number of 45 mm-thick laminations that can be used is 12 (12 × 45 mm = 540 mm deep) but as shear deflection must also be considered, 13 laminations will be used giving $d = 12 × 45$ mm = 585 mm.
A breadth $b$, greater than 117 mm (585 mm/5) must be used, say, $b = 120$ mm giving

$$I = \frac{120 \text{ mm} × 585 \text{ mm}^3}{12} = 2.002 × 10^9 \text{ mm}^4. \tag{6.15}$$

Adding the bending deflection and the shear deflection will give the total deflection:

Bending deflection

$$= \frac{5WL^3}{384EI} = \frac{5 \times 30\,000\,\text{N} \times (10\,000\,\text{mm})^3}{384 \times 11\,025\,\text{N/mm}^2 \times 2.002 \times 10^9\,\text{mm}^4} = 17.70\,\text{mm}.$$

$$\text{Shear deflection} = \frac{3WL}{20Cbd}$$

where $C = E \div 16$ (clause 11)
$$= 11\,025\,\text{N/mm}^2 \div 16 = 689\,\text{N/mm}^2$$

$$\frac{3 \times 30\,000\,\text{N} \times 10\,000\,\text{mm}}{20 \times 689\,\text{N/mm}^2 \times 120\,\text{mm} \times 585\,\text{mm}} = 0.94\,\text{mm}.$$

Total imposed load deflection $= 17.70 + 0.94\,\text{mm} = 18.64\,\text{mm} < 30\,\text{mm}$, therefore satisfactory.

*Bend radius*

The minimum bend radius, $r$, for softwoods is 125 times the lamination thickness (6.5) giving $r \geqslant 125 \times 45\,\text{mm} = 5625\,\text{mm}$. A convenient bend radius would be

$$r = 6000\,\text{mm giving } \frac{r}{t} = \frac{6000}{45} = 133 > 125,$$

therefore satisfactory.
    As $r/t < 250$ (section 6.5), then the bending, tension and compression parallel to the grain grade stresses should be multiplied by the modification factor

$$K33 = 0.76 + 0.001\frac{r}{t}, \text{ where } \frac{r}{t} = \frac{6000}{45} = 133.33,$$

giving $K33 = 0.76 + 0.133 = 0.8933$.
    To calculate the bending stress induced by the applied load bending moment $M$, the ratio of minimum mean radius of curvature $r_{\text{mean}}$ to the depth $h$ must be calculated (section 6.5) and $K34$ determined if the ratio is less than 15. Using Figure 6.1

$$\frac{r_{\text{mean}}}{h} = \frac{6000\,\text{mm} + (585 \div 2)\,\text{mm}}{585\,\text{mm}} = 10.756 < 15.$$

Using

$$K34 = 1.15 - \left(\frac{0.01 r_{mean}}{h}\right) \text{ for } 10 \leqslant \frac{r_{mean}}{h} \leqslant 15$$

gives

$$K34 = 1.15 - (0.01 \times 10.756) = 1.0424.$$

As $K34$ is greater than 1 (section 6.5), the maximum bending stress $\sigma_m$ is in the extreme fibre on the concave inside face of the beam and is found as follows:

$$\sigma_m = K34 \times \frac{6M}{bh^2}$$

where $M$ = apex bending moment due to dead plus imposed load.

$$M = \frac{WL}{8} = \frac{(2.5 \text{ N/mm} + 3.0 \text{ N/mm}) \times 10\,000 \text{ mm} \times 10\,000 \text{ mm}}{8}$$
$$= 68.75 \times 10^6 \text{ N/mm}$$

giving

$$\sigma_m = \frac{1.0424(K34) \times 6 \times 68.75 \times 10^6 \text{ Nmm}}{120 \text{ mm} \times (585 \text{ mm})^2} = 10.47 \text{ N/mm}^2.$$

Permissible bending stress = SS grade stress $\times K15 \times K3 \times K7 \times K33$

where $K15$ = 1.43 (Table 24, LB grade, 13 laminations)
$K3$ = 1.25 (Table 17, medium-term load)
$K7$ = depth factor (section 3.9; clause 14.6)
$$= 0.81 \times \left(\frac{585^2 + 92\,300}{585^2 + 56\,800}\right) = 0.882$$
$K33$ = 0.8933

giving the permissible bending stress

$$= 7.5 \text{ N/mm}^2 \times 1.43 \times 1.25 \times 0.882 \times 0.8933 = 10.562 \text{ N/mm}^2,$$

which is greater than the applied bending stress of 10.47 N/mm², therefore satisfactory.

*Radial stress*

The applied radial stress

$$\sigma_r = \frac{3M}{2bdr_{mean}}$$

$$= \frac{3 \times 68.75 \times 10^6 \text{ N/mm}}{2 \times 120 \text{ mm} \times 585 \text{ mm} \times 6293 \text{ mm}} = 0.233 \text{ N/mm}^2.$$

As the applied bending moment $M$ increases the radius of curvature, the radial stress will be tension perpendicular to the grain, and must not exceed one-third of the permissible shear stress parallel to the grain,

$$= \frac{1}{3} \times 0.82 \text{ N/mm}^2 \times 2.0(K19) \times 1.25(K3) = 0.683 \text{ N/mm}^2.$$

The applied radial stress of 0.233 N/mm² is less than the permissible radial stress of 0.683 N/mm², therefore satisfactory.

*Shear stress*

The applied shear stress parallel to the grain is $3V/2bh$, where

$$V = \frac{(2.5 \text{ kN} + 3 \text{ kN}) \times 10 \text{ m}}{2} = 27.5 \text{ kN}$$

giving

$$\frac{3 \times 27\,500 \text{ N}}{2 \times 120 \text{ mm} \times 585 \text{ mm}} = 0.588 \text{ N/mm}^2.$$

The permissible shear stress is 0.82 N/mm² $\times$ 2.0($K19$) $\times$ 1.25($K3$) = 2.05 N/mm² which is greater than the applied shear stress of 0.588 N/mm², therefore satisfactory.

*Bearing stress*

Assuming a bearing length of 150 mm at the end of the beam, with a bearing width of 120 mm, the applied bearing stress is

$$\frac{27\,500 \text{ N}}{150 \text{ mm} \times 120 \text{ mm}} = 1.528 \text{ N/mm}^2.$$

The permissible bearing stress (section 3.5; clause 14.2) is

2.1 N/mm² $\times$ 1.0($K4$) $\times$ 1.33($K18$) $\times$ 1.25($K3$) $\times$ 1.33 (Table 10, no wane) = 4.643 N/mm²

which is greater than the applied bearing stress of 1.528 N/mm², therefore satisfactory.

*Pre-camber*

The beam must be pre-cambered to offset the dead load bending and shear deflections as follows:

$$\text{Pre-camber} = \frac{5WL^3}{384EI} + \frac{3WL}{20Cbd}$$

$$= \frac{5 \times 25\,000 \times (10\,000 \text{ mm})^3}{384 \times 11\,025 \text{ N/mm}^2 \times 2.002 \times 10^9 \text{ mm}^4}$$

$$+ \frac{3 \times 25\,000 \text{ N} \times 10\,000 \text{ mm}}{20 \times 689 \text{ N/mm}^2 \times 120 \text{ mm} \times 585 \text{ mm}}$$

$$= 14.74 \text{ mm} + 0.775 \text{ mm} = 15.52 \text{ mm pre-camber.}$$

*Joint efficiency*

The end joints must have a bending efficiency rating of at least 70 per cent (section 6.3 (clause 20)), as given in Appendix F, Tables 104 and 105 of BS 5268: Pt 2.

## 6.11 Design example 2: Pitched cambered softwood roof beam

*A rectangular pitched cambered softwood roof beam is to be manufactured from Redwood, grade LB throughout. The beam has an effective span of 10 metres and a pitch of 20°. If the medium-term loading consists of a 2.5 kN/m dead load and a 3.0 kN/m imposed load, determine the beam size and the amount of pre-camber. The beam geometry and loading are symmetrical about the mid-span.*

The relevant SS grade Redwood stresses are:

Bending parallel to the grain $= 7.5$ N/mm$^2$
Shear parallel to the grain $= 0.82$ N/mm$^2$
Compression perpendicular to the grain $= 2.1$ N/mm$^2$
$E$ mean $= 10\,500$ N/mm$^2$.

The limiting live load deflection $= 0.003 \times 10$ m span (section 6.5 (clause 21.2)) $= 30$ mm.

$I$ can be found from the bending deflection $= 30$ mm $= \dfrac{5WL^3}{384EI}$

where

$W$ = 3.0 kN × 10 m = 30 kN
$L$ = 10 m
$E$ = 10 500 N/mm$^2$ × 1.05 ($K$20 from Table 24, LB grade)
= 9450 N/mm$^2$

giving 30 mm = $\dfrac{5 \times 30\ 000\ N \times (10\ 000\ mm)^3}{384 \times 11025\ N/mm^2 \times I}$

$I$ = 1.181 × 10$^9$ mm$^4$.

The ends of the beam will be held in position and, due to the roof decking, the compression edge will be held in line; the maximum ratio of beam depth $d$ to beam width $b$ is 5 (section 3.11 (Table 19)).

Using $\dfrac{d}{b}$ = 5 and $I = \dfrac{bd^3}{12}$ = 1.1810 × 10$^9$ mm$^4$

gives $d$= 515.94 mm and $b$ = 103.19 mm.

Twelve No. 45 mm-thick laminations are 540 mm, but as shear deflection must also be considered, 13 No. 45 mm-thick laminations will be used giving $d$ = 585 mm as shown in Figure 6.3, and $b$ = 117 mm, say, $b$ = 120 mm.

$I$ becomes $\dfrac{120\ mm \times (585\ mm)^3}{12}$ = 2.002 × 10$^9$ mm$^4$.

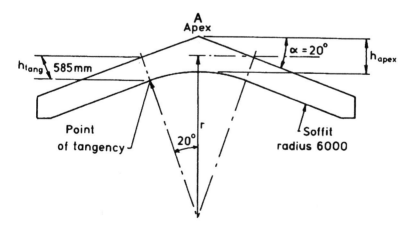

**Figure 6.3 Pitched cambered beam for Design example 2**

Total live load deflection = bending deflection + shear deflection

$$= \frac{5 \times 30\,000 \text{ N} \times (10\,000 \text{ mm})^3}{384 \times 11025 \text{ N/mm}^2 \times 2.002 \times 10^9 \text{ mm}^4}$$

$$+ \frac{3 \times 30\,000 \text{ N} \times 10\,000 \text{ mm}}{20 \times 689 \text{ N/mm}^2 \times 120 \text{ mm} \times 585 \text{ mm}}$$

$$= 17.70 \text{ mm} + 0.931 \text{ mm} = 18.63 \text{ mm deflection}$$

which is less than 30 mm, therefore satisfactory.

The required dead load deflection is found by replacing the 30 kN live load by the 25 kN dead load in the live load deflection equation giving the pre-camber as 14.34 mm + 0.753 mm = 15.526 mm pre-camber.

*Bend radius*

The minimum bend radius, $r$, for softwoods is 125 times the lamination thickness (section 6.5) giving 125 × 45 mm = 5625 mm. A convenient radius greater than the minimum would be 6000 mm, as shown in Figure 6.3, which would give the soffit radius.

*Apex bending stress*

The apex bending stress $\sigma_{m,apex}$ is at a maximum at the soffit and is calculated from (section 6.6 (clause 21.4)):

$$\sigma_{m,apex} = \frac{(1.0 + 2.7 \tan \alpha)\, 6M_{apex}}{bh_{apex}^2}$$

where $\alpha = 20°$

$$M_{apex} = 68.75 \times 10^6 \text{ Nmm} = \frac{(25 \text{ kN} + 30 \text{ kN}) \times 10 \text{ m}}{8}$$

$b = 120$ mm, but must not be less than $h_{apex} \div 5$ (Table 19) $h_{apex}$ is determined as follows:

$$\text{radius to apex A} = \frac{6000 \text{ mm} + 585 \text{ mm}}{\cos 20°} = 7008 \text{ mm (Figure 6.3)}$$

giving $h_{apex} = 7008$ mm − 6000 mm = 1008, say, 1000 mm and $b = 1000 \div 5 = 200$ mm.

$$\sigma_{m,apex} = \frac{(1.0 + 0.982) \times 6 \times 68.75 \times 10^6 \text{ Nmm}}{200 \times 1000 \text{ mm}^2}$$

$$= 4.09 \text{ N/mm}^2.$$

The permissible bending stress

= SS grade stress $\times K15 \times K3 \times K7 = 7.5 \text{ N/mm}^2 \times 1.43(K15) \times 1.25(K3) \times 0.837(K7) = 11.221 \text{ N/mm}^2$,

where $K15 = 1.43$ (Table 22, LB grade 13 laminations), $K3 = 1.25$ (Table 15 medium-term load), and $K7$ = depth factor (section 3.9, clause 14.6) ($h = 1000$ mm) $= 0.837$.

The permissible bending stress of 11.221 N/mm$^2$ is greater than the applied bending apex stress of 4.09 N/mm$^2$, therefore satisfactory.

*Tangent point bending stress*

The applied bending stress at the tangent point is found from

$$\sigma_{m,tang} = \frac{6M_{tang}}{bd_{tang}^2}$$

where $M_{tang}$ = the bending moment at the point of tangency. The point of tangency is 6000 mm sin 20° from the centre line = 2052 mm, and is (10 m $\div$ 2) − 2.052 m = 2.948 m from the support.

Taking moments about the point of tangency.

$$M_{tang} = \frac{2.948 \text{ m} \times ((2.5 \text{ kN/m} + 3.0 \text{ kN/m}) \times 10 \text{ m})}{2}$$
$$- \left(5.5 \text{ kN/m} \times \frac{2.948 \text{ m}^2}{2}\right)$$

$$= (81.07 \text{ kNm}) - (23.899 \text{ kNm}) = 57.171 \times 10^6 \text{ Nmm}$$

giving

$$\sigma_{m,tang} = \frac{6 \times 57.171 \times 10^6 \text{ Nmm}}{200 \text{ mm} \times 585 \text{ mm}^2} = 5.012 \text{ N/mm}^2.$$

The permissible stress at the point of tangency

$$= 7.5 \text{ N/mm}^2 \times 1.43(K15) \times 1.25(K3) \times 0.882(K7)$$
$$= 11.824 \text{ N/mm}^2$$

where $K7 = 2$ depth factor (section 3.9, clause 14.6) ($h = 585$ mm) $= 0.882$.

**111**

The applied bending stress at the point of tangency is 5.012 N/mm$^2$ and is less than the permissible bending stress of 11.824 N/mm$^2$, therefore satisfactory.

## Radial stress

The radial stress $\sigma_r$ is at a maximum near the mid-depth at the apex (section 6.6, clause 21.4) and is taken as the larger of the two following values:

$$\sigma_r = \frac{(K35)6M_{\text{apex}}}{bh^2_{\text{apex}}} \text{ or } \frac{3M_{\text{apex}}}{2rbh_{\text{apex}}}$$

where $M_{\text{apex}}$ = $68.75 \times 10^6$ Nmm

$b$ = 200 mm

$h_{\text{apex}}$ = 1000 mm

$r$ = radius of curvature at the centre line of the apex depth

= 6000 mm + (1000 mm/2) = 6500 mm

$K35$ = $A + B\,(h_{\text{apex}}/r) + C\,(h_{\text{apex}}/r)^2$

where A, B and C are taken from Table 28.

$\alpha$ = roof slope = 20° giving

$K35 = 0.089 + 0.061\,(1000 \text{ mm}/6500 \text{ mm}) + 0.139\,(1000 \text{ mm}/6500 \text{ mm})^2$
= 0.1017 giving

$$\sigma_r = \frac{0.1017 \times 6 \times 68.75 \times 10^6 \text{ Nmm}}{200 \text{ mm} \times (1000 \text{ mm})^2} = 0.210 \text{ N/mm}^2$$

or $\dfrac{3 \times 68.75 \times 10^6 \text{ Nmm}}{2 \times 6500 \text{ mm} \times 200 \times 1000 \text{ mm}} = 0.079 \text{ N/mm}^2$

therefore applied radial stress is 0.210 N/mm$^2$ due to $M_{\text{apex}}$ and must not be greater than one-third of the permissible shear parallel to the grain

$$= \frac{1}{3} \times 0.82 \text{ N/mm}^2 \times 2.00(K19) \times 1.25(K3) = 0.683 \text{ N/mm}^2,$$

which is greater than the applied radial stress of 0.210 N/mm$^2$, therefore satisfactory.

**112**

*Tangent point radial stress*

The tangent point radial stress is found from (section 6.5 (clause 21.3.3)):

$$\sigma_r = \frac{3M_{tang}}{2bhr_{mean}} = \frac{3 \times 57.171 \times 10^6 \text{ Nmm}}{2 \times 200 \text{ mm} \times 585 \text{ mm} \times 6500 \text{ mm}} = 0.113 \text{ N/mm}^2$$

which is less than the permissible radial stress of $0.682 \text{ N/mm}^2$, therefore satisfactory.

*Support shear stress*

The applied shear stress parallel to the grain is found from $3V/2bh$ where $V = (2.5 \text{ kN} + 3.0 \text{ kN}) \times 10 \text{ m})/2 = 27\ 500 \text{ N}$, $b = 200 \text{ m}$, and $h = 585 \text{ mm}$, giving

$$\frac{3 \times 27\ 500 \text{ N}}{2 \times 200 \text{ mm} \times 585 \text{ mm}} = 0.353 \text{ N/mm}^2$$

The permissible shear stress $= 0.82 \text{ N/mm}^2 \times 2.0(K19) \times 1.25(K3) = 2.05 \text{ N/mm}^2$, which is greater than the applied shear stress of $0.353 \text{ N/mm}^2$, therefore satisfactory.

*Bearing stress*

Assuming a bearing length of 150 mm at the end of the beam and a bearing width of 200 mm, the applied bearing stress is

$$\frac{27\ 500 \text{ N}}{150 \text{ mm} \times 200 \text{ mm}} = 0.917 \text{ N/mm}^2.$$

The permissible bearing stress (section 3.5, clause 14.2) is

$2.1 \text{ N/mm}^2 \times 1.0(K4) \times 1.33(K18) \times 1.25(K3) \times 1.33$ (Table 9, no wane) $= 4.643 \text{ N/mm}^2$

which is greater than the applied bearing stress of $0.913 \text{ N/mm}^2$, therefore satisfactory.

*Joint efficiency*

The end joints must have a bending efficiency rating of at least 70 per cent (section 6.3 (clause 20)) as given in Appendix F, Tables 104 and 105.

*Deflection*

As the beam has been increased in width from 120 to 200 mm, the live load deflection and the amount of pre-camber must be redetermined using the bending and shear deflection and will be found to be:

$$\frac{5 \times 30\ 000\ \text{N} \times (10\ 000\ \text{mm})^3 \times 120\ \text{mm}}{384 \times 11\ 025\ \text{N/mm}^2 \times 2.002 \times 10^9\ \text{mm}^4 \times 200\ \text{mm}}$$

$$+ \frac{3 \times 30\ 000\ \text{N} \times 10\ 000\ \text{mm}}{20 \times 689\ \text{N/mm}^2 \times 200\ \text{mm} \times 585\ \text{m}}$$

$$= 10.62\ \text{mm} + 0.558\ \text{mm} = 11.18\ \text{mm deflection}$$

and a pre-camber of $11.18\ \text{mm} \times \dfrac{25\ \text{kN}}{30\ \text{kN}} = 9.31\ \text{mm}$.

*Conclusion*

As the beam width had to be increased from 120 to 200 mm the beam is very much oversized. For example, the highest ratio of applied stress to permissible stress is the apex bending stress and is

$$\frac{4.09\ \text{N/mm}^2}{11.221\ \text{N/mm}^2} = 0.364$$

while the ratio of applied deflection to permissible deflection is

$$\frac{11.18\ \text{mm}}{30\ \text{mm}} = 0.373$$

To use the beam more efficiently the designer can either increase the loading on the beam, by increasing the distance between roof beams, or reduce the $I$ value of the beam.

# 7 Plywood

## 7.1 Introduction

Both sanded and unsanded plywoods manufactured in accordance with the standards listed in clause 4 and on page 126 of BS 5268: Pt 2, subjected to the quality control procedures of the organizations listed in clause 24, may be used for structural purposes. Special-purpose plywoods and plywoods with unbalanced geometrical construction are not covered in BS 5268: Pt 2.

In specifying plywood, the type, grade, nominal thickness, number of plies and whether sanded or unsanded needs to be given, remembering that for each nominal thickness and number of plies a range of constructions, combining plies of different thicknesses, is available.

The strength and stiffness of plywood is expressed in terms of a full cross-section stress, while the section properties are given for the minimum strength construction for each specification. The strength capacity and stiffness are found by multiplying the section stress and modulus of elasticity by the appropriate section property.

Appendix B of BS 5268: Pt 2 gives the timber species used in the manufacture of plywoods.

## 7.2 Durability

All plywoods specified in BS 5268: Pt 2 are bonded with an exterior-type adhesive, but consideration must be given to the natural durability of the species used for the plywood. If the plywood is to be used for permanent structures in damp or wet conditions, it must be adequately treated against decay unless the species is inherently durable. American construction plywood, C-D grade with exterior glue should not be used in prolonged damp or wet conditions.

## 7.3  Dimension and section properties

Table 7.1 lists the titles of Tables 29 to 38 of BS 5268: Pt 2. These tables give the section properties of the plywoods based on their permitted minimum thicknesses and apply to both the wet and dry exposure conditions.

### Table 7.1  Section properties of plywoods

| Table no. | Section properties of |
|---|---|
| 29 | American construction and industrial plywood: unsanded |
| 30 | American construction and industrial plywood: sanded |
| 31 | British hardwood plywood: sanded |
| 32 | Canadian Douglas fir and softwood plywoods: unsanded |
| 33 | Canadian Douglas fir plywood: sanded |
| 34 | Finnish birch plywood: sanded |
| 35 | Finnish birch-faced plywood: sanded |
| 36 | Finnish conifer plywood: sanded |
| 37 | Swedish softwood plywood: unsanded |
| 38 | Swedish softwood plywood: sanded |

## 7.4  Grades

The grade stresses for plywoods only apply to the American construction and industrial plywoods, British hardwood plywoods, Canadian Douglas fir and softwood plywoods, Finnish birch, birch-faced and conifer plywoods, together with Swedish softwood plywoods, bearing the identification marks specified in clause 27.

## 7.5  Grade stresses

The grade stresses given in Tables 39 to 52 of BS 5268: Pt 2 apply to the long-term loading in the dry exposure condition and must be used in conjunction with the corresponding section properties given in Tables 29 to 38. For the wet exposure condition, the stresses are modified by $K36$ given in Table 51. Table 7.2 lists the titles of Tables 39 to 52.

**Table 7.2  Dry grade stresses and moduli**

| Table no. | Dry grade stresses and moduli for |
|---|---|
| 39 | American construction and industrial plywood: C-D grade. Exposure 1: unsanded |
| 40 | American construction and industrial plywood: C-D grade. Exposure 1: unsanded |
| 41 | American construction and industrial plywood: A-C/B-C grades. Exterior sanded |
| 42 | British hardwood plywood: sanded |
| 43 | Canadian Douglas fir plywood: select tight face, select and sheathing grades: unsanded |
| 44 | Canadian Douglas fir plywood: good two sides and good one side grades: sanded |
| 45 | Canadian softwood plywood: select tight face, select and sheathing grades: unsanded |
| 46 | Finnish birch plywood: I/I, I/II,I/III,II/II,II/III,III/III,III/IV, and IV/IV grades: sanded |
| 47 | Finnish birch-faced plywood: I/I, I/II, I/III, II/II, II/III, III/III, III/IV, and IV/IV grades: sanded |
| 48 | Finnish conifer plywood: I/I, I/II, I/III, II/II, II/III, III/III, III/IV and IV/IV grades: sanded |
| 49 | Swedish softwood plywood: P30 grade: unsanded |
| 50 | Swedish softwood plywood: P30 grade: sanded |
| 51 | Swedish softwood plywood: P40 grade: unsanded |
| 52 | Swedish softwood plywood: P40 grade: sanded |

In the case of American construction and industrial plywoods, grades C-D unsanded, C-C unsanded, A-C sanded and B-C sanded of Tables 39, 40 and 41 respectively, the bending, tension and compression stresses should be reduced in proportion to their width for widths between 600 mm (no reduction) and 200 mm and less (50 per cent reduction).

## 7.6  Duration of loading

The grade stresses given in Tables 39 to 52 apply to the long-term loading. For other durations of loading, the value of the modification factor $K3$ is given in Table 2.1, but does not apply to the modulus of elasticity or the shear modulus.

## 7.7 Flexural members

Plywood flexural members are particularly efficient. They combine lightness with the ability to span distances larger than normally available in solid timber beam sections. The plywood is used to resist the shear in the webs with the solid timber being used as the top and bottom flanges to resist the applied bending forces. In addition to the plywood webs, vertical web stiffeners are also added to counteract web buckling due to heavy point loads.

The design of plywood flexural members is dealt with in sections 3.16 and 3.25.

## 7.8 Special plywood properties

In plywood, consideration must be given to two additional forms of shear failure, namely panel shear and rolling shear. In solid timber, the panel shear of plywood is similar to the horizontal shear failure along the grain parallel to the neutral axis that may occur in deep, short-span beams which are restrained to prevent lateral buckling.

For plywood web flexural members, supported by flanges and stiffeners, the panel shear failure through the thickness is altered due to the odd number of plies being arranged at 90° to each other. Consequently some plies will fail and other plies at 90° may not fail. This distribution of panel shear failure is due to the different plywood properties related to the number of veneers being either parallel or perpendicular to the face grain. For rolling shear, the timber in the plies at 90° to the applied principal shear force tend to roll and cause failure. The calculations for both forms of shear failure are dealt with in section 3.25.

# 8  Tempered hardboard

## 8.1  Introduction

Only TE grade tempered hardboard of nominal thickness from 3.2 to 8 mm, complying with BS 1142: Pt 2 can be used for structural purposes, when designing to BS 5268: Pt 2.

Tempered hardboard, because it is relatively dry and will take up water, must be conditioned two or three days before fixing by applying water uniformly by brush or mop to the mesh face at the rate of 0.5 litre for every 3.2 mm thickness for a board size of 1220 × 2440 mm. After applying the water, the boards should be stacked, mesh faces together on a flat surface, away from sunlight and heat sources. Tempered hardboard that is not conditioned and is securely fixed to a rigid framework will expand and buckle if it were to take up moisture.

The information in BS 5268: Pt 2 relates only to tempered hardboard used in stressed members where the service condition would justify the use of the dry stress values. It should not be used structurally in continuously wet or immersed conditions.

## 8.2  Durability

The risk of rot is low as fungi will only attack the board where the moisture content is well above the equilibrium moisture content they will achieve in a saturated atmosphere. Provided the board is not exposed to damp or wet conditions, no further protection by preservative treatment is needed. Wood-boring insects normally found in the United Kingdom will not attack tempered hardboard.

## 8.3   Dimensions and section properties

Table 54 (BS 5268: Pt 2) gives the section properties of tempered hardboard, based on the minimum permitted thicknesses. If the actual thickness is greater, this may be used to calculate the section properties.

## 8.4   Grade stresses

The grade stresses for tempered hardboard are given in Table 3.8 (Table 55) and apply to the long-term loading in the dry exposure condition. Tables 54 and 55 should be used together.

## 8.5   Duration of load

The grade stresses of Table 55 are modified by the duration of load factor $K38$ as given in Table 2.1. Where a value of $K38$ greater than 1.00 is used, all conditions of loading must be checked. The modulus of elasticity and the shear modulus are not multiplied by $K38$.

Creep plays a considerable part in the calculations relating to tempered hardboard, and Table 57 gives the modification factors $K39$, $K40$ and $K41$ that must be applied to the modulus of elasticity and shear modulus for the net long-term loads, the net medium-term loads and the net short- or net very short-term loads, respectively. The net loads are the loads of stated duration only. For example, the net medium-term load would be either the snow load or the temporary imposed load.

In determining the deflections or the deformation of the structural members, subjected to a combination of loads of different duration, each load duration category must be considered as acting separately, and the deflections induced calculated separately. The values for the elastic moduli are determined for each load duration category by multiplying the elastic modulus given in Table 3.8 (Table 55) by the appropriate modification factor from Table 57. The total deflection is the sum of the deflections caused by the individual loads.

## 8.6   Flexural members

The design of tempered hardboard flexural members is dealt with in sections 3.17 and 3.26.

# 9  Joints

## 9.1  Introduction

Joints must be designed such that the load carried by each nail, screw, bolt or connector due to the design loads does not exceed the permissible values. The basic loads for single fasteners, subjected to long-term dry exposure loading are given in Section 6 of BS 5268: Pt 2. The permissible loads for other conditions, types of loading and joint geometry are determined by multiplying the basic loads by the appropriate modification factors.

The joint loads are tabulated for the strength classes given in section 1.3 (BS 5268: Pt 2, clause 10), but in assigning joint loads to the strength classes, there are the following exceptions:

1  All softwoods of SC5, except pitch pine and southern pine (USA), should use the fastener loads given for strength classes SC3 and SC4.
2  All grades of British-grown Sitka spruce, British-grown European spruce, Canadian Sitka Spruce and western whitewoods (USA) should use the fastener loads given for strength classes SC1 and SC2.
3  For grades of hem-fir (USA) and spruce-pine-fir (Canada) of strength classes other than SC1 and SC2, the values of lateral load perpendicular to the grain for bolts and timber connectors should be multiplied by the joint/class modification factor $K42$ equal to 0.9.

For mechanical fasteners in glued laminated timber, the permissible loads should be those appropriate to the strength class of the species SS grade or hardwood HS grade unless clause 38 (BS 5268: Pt 2) reduces these permissible loads.

4  For all strength classes of machine-graded radiata pine (New Zealand), the values of lateral load for bolts and timber connectors should be those tabulated for SC1 and SC2.

The effective cross-section and not the gross cross-section is used when calculating the joint strength.

If more than one fastener is used at a joint, due account must be taken of the relative stiffnesses of the fasteners.

All edge distances, end distances and fastener spacings refer to the distances from the fastener centre lines.

Where it can be ensured the timber contains no visible strength-reducing characteristics at the joint positions, the clear wood stresses should be used. The clear wood stresses are found by multiplying the appropriate modification factor of Table 106 of BS 5268: Pt 2 by the relevant SS or HS grade value from Tables 10 or 15 respectively, but within the limitations of 1 to 4 above.

## 9.2  Secondary stresses

Secondary stresses will be induced if the line of action of the applied force does not pass through the centroid of the fastener group. These secondary stresses must be taken into account.

Care must be taken to ensure that any splitting of a wide member that may dry out after jointing has been accommodated in the joint design.

## 9.3  Anti-corrosion treatment

Care must be taken to ensure that any anti-corrosion treatment applied to the timber does not affect the fastener performance, nor corrode the fastener. The loads given for nails, screws and bolts assume the timber has not been treated against corrosion, but the loads given for timber connectors assume that the fasteners have been treated against corrosion.

Fasteners used for timber exposed to the wet exposure condition or to be used wet, must be non-corrodible or be treated by an anti-corrosive process.

## 9.4 Nailed joints

A nailed joint usually consists of at least two nails. The nails, if used in timber of strength classes SC6, SC7, SC8 or SC9, will often need pre-drilling. The diameter of the pre-drilled hole should not be greater than 80 per cent of the nail diameter.

Skew nailing may increase the withdrawal resistance, but should not be used if the nail is laterally loaded unless there is no in-service stress reversal or the applied load will tend to tighten the joint. Opposed double skew nailing is preferable to parallel skew nailing.

### 9.4.1 Effective cross-section

For nails of less than 5 mm cross-section, driven without pre-drilling, no reduction of cross-section is required. For multiple nailing, all the nails that lie within a distance of five nail diameters, measured parallel to the grain, from a given cross-section are considered as occurring at that cross-section, and their net projected area is deducted from the gross cross-section area to determine the effective cross-section.

### 9.4.2 Nail spacing

To avoid splitting, the minimum end distances, edge distances and nail spacings are given in Table 9.1, where $d$ is the nail diameter.

With all softwoods in strength classes SC1 to SC5, except Douglas fir, the spacing for timber-to-timber joints, given in Table 9.1, should be multiplied by 0.8. Where nails have been driven at right-angles to the glued surfaces of pre-glued laminated members, the spacings may be further multiplied by 0.9. In no case must the edge distance in the timber be less than $5d$.

### 9.4.3 Timber-to-timber joints

The permissible joint load is found from the basic load modified in accordance with BS 5268: Pt 2, clause 41.8.

Table 59 (BS 5268: Pt 2) gives the basic single shear lateral loads for round wire nails driven at right-angles to the side grain of dry timber. The table lists the nail diameter, the standard member headside and pointside thicknesses together with the strength classes divided into four groups as follows: SC1 and SC2; SC3 and SC4; SC5; the remaining strength classes SC6, SC7, SC8 and SC9. The nail must penetrate the headside thickness and at least the thickness given for the pointside. If the standard headside or pointside thicknesses are not attained, then the

## Table 9.1   Minimum nail spacings

| | Joint type | | | |
|---|---|---|---|---|
| | Timber-to-timber | | Steel plate-to-timber | Plywood tempered, hardboard or chipboard-to-timber |
| Pre-drilled: | No | Yes | No | No |
| End distance parallel to grain | 20d | 10d | 14d | 14d |
| Edge distance perpendicular to grain | 5d | 5d | 5d | |
| | | | | timber 5d<br>plywood 3d<br>hardboard $\}$<br>chipboard $\}$ 6d |
| Distance between lines of nails, perpendicular to the grain | 10d | 3d | 7d | 7d |
| Distance between adjacent nails in any one line, parallel to the grain | 20d | 10d | 14d | 14d |

Note: $d$ is the nail diameter
Source: Reproduced with permission from BS 5268: Pt 2

Table 57 value must be reduced by the smaller of the two following ratios:

1   actual to standard thickness of headside members; or
2   actual penetration to standard pointside thickness.

No increase in the values is allowed if the member thickness is greater than the standard value.

For nails driven into the end grain, the values of Tables 59 are multiplied by the end-grain modification factor $K43$ which equals 0.7. For a joint with more than one shear plane, the basic multiple shear lateral load for each nail is found by multiplying the given value of Table 59 by 0.9 times the number of shear planes. Each member must have a joint thickness of at least 0.7 times the standard thickness of the pointside member.

The basic withdrawal loads for single nails at right-angles to the side grain of dry timber are given in Table 60. The values in Table 60 must be multiplied by the pointside penetration in millimetres. The minimum penetration must be 15 mm.

No nail, whether of improved type or not, should be used to carry withdrawal load when driven into end grain.

Improved nails which are square grooved or twisted shank and have a yield stress not less than 375 N/mm$^2$ have their basic lateral loads given in Table 59 multiplied by the improved nail lateral modification factor $K44$. $K44$ has the value 1.25. The nominal nail diameter is 0.75 multiplied by the diagonal. $K44$ is replaced by $K45$ equal to 1.5, when considering the withdrawal loads of Table 60 using the threaded part of the annular-shank and helical-threaded shank nails.

### 9.4.4 Steel plate-to-timber joints

The basic lateral load given in Table 59 is multiplied by the steel-to-timber modification factor $K46$, which equals 1.25, provided the pre-drilled nail holes in the steel plate are no larger than the nail diameter.

### 9.4.5 Plywood-to-timber joints

The plywood must be selected from those described in Chapter 7 (BS 5268: Pt 2, Section 4). The basic single shear lateral loads for single nails in plywood-to-timber joints where the nails are driven through the plywood at right-angles into the side grain of dry timber are given in Table 61. For plywood thicknesses other than 6 mm the basic loads are found from:

$$F + K47(t - 6)$$

where $F$ is the basic lateral load in newtons obtained from Table 61, $K47$ is the modification factor obtained from Table 62 and $t$ is the nominal plywood thickness (mm). For the basic loads to apply, the nails must be fully embedded and have a length of not less than that shown in Table 9.2.

### 9.4.6 Tempered hardboard-to-timber joints

The tempered hardboard must be in accordance with that described in Chapter 8 (BS 5268: Pt 2, Section 5). The basic single shear lateral loads

## Table 9.2   Nail length

| Nail diameter (mm) | Length (mm) | or | Nominal plywood thickness plus additional length (mm) |
|---|---|---|---|
| 2.65 | 40 | | 25 |
| 3.00 | 45 | | 29 |
| 3.35 | 45 | | 32 |
| 3.75 | 55 | | 38 |
| 4.00 | 60 | | 44 |

for single nails in tempered hardboard-to-timber joints where the nails are driven through the hardboard at right-angles into the side grain of dry timber are given in Table 63. For the basic loads to apply, the nails must be fully embedded and have an overall length not less than that given in the length column of Table 9.2.

### 9.4.7   Chipboard-to-timber joints

The chipboard must be in accordance with Chapter 12 (BS 5268: Pt 2, Section 9). The basic single shear lateral load for nails in a wood chipboard-to-timber joint where the nails are driven through the chipboard at right-angles into the side grain of dry timber are given in Table 63a. For the basic loads to apply, the nails must be fully embedded with adequate pointside penetration of the nail into the timber. Round wire nails are generally available in standard lengths, which, for the majority of chipboard thicknesses, ensures the required pointside penetration is achieved. Thus the BS does not give recommendations for the modification of basic loads for penetrations less than those required.

For the Table 63a basic loads to apply, the overall nail length should be not less than 2.5 times the 6 mm to 19 mm nominal chipboard thickness or 2.0 times the 20 mm to 40 mm nominal chipboard thickness.

### 9.4.8   Permissible joint loads

The permissible load for a nailed joint is found from the permissible load for each nail in the joint using the following equation:

basic load $\times K48 \times K49 \times K50$.

$K48$ is the modification factor for load duration and has the following values:

| Long-term load | 1.0 |
| --- | --- |
| Medium-term load | 1.25 for tempered hardboard-to-timber joints |
| | 1.40 for chipboard-to-timber joints |
| | 1.12 for all other medium-term loads |
| Short-term and very short-term loads | 1.62 for tempered hardboard-to-timber joints |
| | 2.10 for chipboard-to-timber joints |
| | 1.25 for all other short-term and very short-term loads |

$K49$ is the modification factor for moisture content and has the following values:

1.0   1   for a joint in dry timber
     2   for annular-ringed shank and helical-threaded shank nails under all exposure conditions, and
     3   for withdrawal loads under constant wet or dry exposure conditions
     4   for chipboard-to-timber
0.7    for lateral loads in green timber
0.25   for withdrawal loads where cyclic changes in moisture content can occur after nailing

$K50$ is the modification factor for the number of nails in each line and has the following values:

If the nails

1   have the same diameter
2   are acting in single or multiple shear
3   are symmetrically arranged in lines parallel to the line of action of the load in a primarily loaded member in a structural framework, then

$K50 = 1.0$ for $n < 10$
$K50 = 0.9$ for $n \geqslant 10$

where $n$ is the number of nails in each line.

In all other cases, where more than one nail is used in a joint

$K50 = 1.0$

## 9.5  Screwed joints

Steel screws must comply with BS 1210: *Wood screws.* Screws must be turned, using a non-corrosive lubricant if necessary, into pre-drilled holes. The top of the countersunk screws must be no more than 1 mm below the timber surface.

The hole for the shank shall have the same diameter as the shank diameter and be no deeper than the shank length. For the threaded portion of the screw the hole diameter should be 40 or 60 per cent of the shank diameter for softwoods and hardwoods respectively.

### 9.5.1  Effective cross-section

The effective cross-section is determined by deducting the net projected area of the pre-drilled holes from the gross area of the cross-section being considered. All screws that lie within a distance of five screw diameters measured parallel to the grain from the cross-section being considered, are assumed to be at that cross-section.

### 9.5.2  Screw spacing

To avoid undue timber splitting, Table 9.3 gives the minimum screw spacing, using pre-drilled holes.

### Table 9.3  Minimum screw spacing

| Spacing | Parallel to grain | Perpendicular to grain |
|---|---|---|
| End distance | $10d$ | – |
| Edge distance | – | $5d$ |
| Distance between lines of screws | – | $3d$ |
| Distance between adjacent screws in any one line | $10d$ | – |

Note: $d$ is the screw shank diameter.
Source: Reproduced with permission from BS 5268: Pt 2

### 9.5.3  Permissible load

The permissible load for a screwed joint is determined from the basic loads for each screw modified in accordance with section 9.5.9 (BS 5268: Pt 2, clause 42.7).

## 9.5.4 Timber-to-timber joints

The basic single shear lateral load for single screws inserted at right-angles to the side grain of dry timber are given in BS 5268: Pt 2, Table 65. The screws must fully penetrate the tabulated headside member standard thickness and at least the tabulated pointside penetration distance. If the member thickness or penetration distance is less than the values given in Table 65, then the basic loads are multiplied by the smaller of the following two ratios:

1   actual to standard thickness of the headside member, or
2   actual penetration of the point to the standard pointside thickness.

The basic loads may not be increased for additional thicknesses or penetration, but the minimum pointside penetration must be at least 60 per cent of the tabulated values.

For screws inserted into the end grain, the values given in Table 65 are multiplied by 0.7, the end-grain modification factor.

The basic withdrawal loads for single screws inserted at right-angles to the side grain of dry timber are given in Table 66. The values apply to each 1 mm of penetration and should be multiplied by the actual pointside penetration of the particular screw's threaded part. The minimum screw penetration is 15 mm.

No screw turned into end grain may carry a withdrawal load.

## 9.5.5 Steel plate-to-timber joints

The steel plate should have adequate strength and be designed in accordance with BS 449: Pt 2. The hole diameter should be not greater than the screw shank diameter.

## 9.5.6 Basic loads

For a screw going through a pre-drilled holed in a steel plate into a timber member, the basic lateral load given in Table 65 is multiplied by 1.25, the steel-to-timber modification factor $K46$.

## 9.5.7 Plywood-to-timber joints

The plywood must be one of those specified in Chapter 7 (BS 5268: Pt 2, clauses 24 to 30), with pre-drilled holes no greater than the screw shank diameter.

### 9.5.8 Basic loads

The basic single shear lateral loads for single screws in a 6 mm-thick plywood-to-timber joint where the screws are inserted through the plywood at right-angles on to the side grain of dry timber are given in Table 67 (BS 5268: Pt 2).

For plywoods over 6 mm thick and up to 20 mm thick, the basic loads are calculated from the expression:

$$F + K51(t - 6)$$

where $F$ is the basic lateral load in Newtons as given in Table 67, $t$ is the nominal plywood thickness in mm, and $K51$ a modification factor obtained from Table 66.

For the basic loads to apply, the minimum total screw length should be the greater of the values given in Table 9.4.

#### Table 9.4  Minimum total screw length

| Screw diameter (mm) | Minimum total screw length (mm) | or | Nominal plywood thickness plus (mm) |
|---|---|---|---|
| 4.17 | 38 | | 29 |
| 4.88 | 44 | | 34 |
| 5.59 | 51 | | 39 |

### 9.5.9 Permissible load for a joint

The permissible load for a screwed joint is the sum of the permissible loads for each screw in a joint which equals:

basic load $\times K52 \times K53 \times K54$.

The modification factor for the load duration $K52$ equals

| | |
|---|---|
| Long-term loads | 1.0 |
| Medium-term loads | 1.12 |
| Short-term and very short-term loads | 1.25 |

The modification factor for moisture content $K53$ equals

130

| Joints in dry timber | 1.0 |
| Joints in green timber or timber which will be under wet exposure condition | 0.7 |

The modification factor for the number of screws in each line, $K54$, equals

1.0 for $n < 10$, or
0.9 for $n \geqslant 10$

where $n$ is the number of screws in each line. The number of screws of the same diameter acting in single or multiple shear must be symmetrically arranged in one or more lines parallel to the line of action of the load in a primarily axially-loaded member in a structural framework (clause 5.11).

In all other loading cases, where more than one screw is used in a joint, $K54 = 1.0$.

## 9.6 Bolted joints

Black bolts must comply with BS 4190: *ISO Metric black hexagon bolts, screws and nuts*. The bolt holes should be no more than 2 mm greater than the nominal bolt diameter and preferably as close to the bolt diameter as possible. Washers should comply with BS 4320: *Metal washers for general engineering purposes*, and have a thickness of at least 25 per cent of the bolt diameter. The washers may be circular or square, but must have a diameter or a side length of at least three bolt diameters. No washers are needed if an equivalent bearing area is provided.

### 9.6.1 Effective cross-section

All bolts that lie within two bolt diameters measured parallel to the grain from a given cross-section are considered to occur at that cross-section and their net projected bolt hole area is deducted from the gross area to determine the effective cros- section.

### 9.6.2 Bolt spacing

The minimum bolt spacings are given in Table 9.5 with Table 9.6 giving the minimum edge and end distances.

When a load is applied at an angle to the grain, or when a bolt group resists a moment, the larger of the spacings of Table 9.5 are used. When a joint resists a moment, there will be resulting direct forces and Table 9.6 must be adhered to.

### Table 9.5 Minimum bolt spacing

| Loading type | Minimum bolt spacing |
| --- | --- |
| 1 Spacing in direction of load. | $4d$ |
| 2 Spacing across the grain, between bolts or rows of bolts for loading parallel to the grain. | $4d$ |
| 3 Loading perpendicular to the grain with spacing parallel to the grain between bolts or rows of bolts. | (a) $3d$ where ratio of member thickness $t$ to $d$ is one, or <br> (b) $5d$ where the ratio is three or more. <br> (c) Where the ratio is between one and three, linear interpolation is allowed. |
| 4 Two timber members bolted together at right-angles to each other. | The greater of (a) or (b) above. |

Note: $d$ is the bolt diameter

### Table 9.6 Edge and end distances

| Loading type | Minimum bolt distance |
| --- | --- |
| 1 From end of timber to the centre of the nearest bolt hole for loading parallel to the grain. | (a) $4d$ for bolts bearing away from the member end, or <br> (b) $7d$ for bolts bearing towards the end of the timber. |
| 2 Edge distance of the timber to the centre of the nearest bolt hole. | $5d$ unless the loading is perpendicular to the grain, then the loaded grain must be at least $4d$. |

Note: $d$ is the bolt diameter

### 9.6.3 Timber-to-timber joints

The basic loads for single bolts in a two-member timber joint where the load acts perpendicular to the bolt axis and parallel or perpendicular to the timber grain are given in Table 69 (BS 5268: Pt 2).

The basic load $F$ for a load inclined at an angle $\alpha$ to the timber grain is found from:

$$F = \frac{F_\parallel \times F_\perp}{(F_\parallel \sin^2 \alpha \times F_\perp \cos^2 \alpha)}$$

where $F_\parallel$ is the basic load parallel to the grain as given in Table 69 and $F_\perp$ is the basic load perpendicular to the grain as given in Table 69.

$F$ is also the maximum for the component of the load perpendicular to the bolt axis for loads acting at an angle to the bolt axis.

The thinner member of parallel members determines the joint load, but if unequal-thickness members are joined at an angle, the basic load for each member must be determined and the smaller value used.

For joints of more than two members, the basic load is the sum of the basic load for each shear plane, provided that any member with two shear planes has twice the tabulated thickness.

### 9.6.4 Steel plate-to-timber joints

The steel plate should have adequate strength and be designed in accordance with BS 449: Pt 2.

The hole diameter in the timber and steel must be no more than the bolt diameter plus 2 mm, and preferably as near the bolt diameter as possible.

### 9.6.5 Basic load

When the timber member is loaded parallel to the grain, the basic load given in Table 69 is multiplied by 1.25, the steel-to-timber modification factor $K46$. $K46$ is not applied to timber loaded perpendicular to the grain.

### 9.6.6 Permissible joint load

The permissible load for a bolted joint is the sum of the permissible load for each bolt in the joint which equals:

basic load $\times K55 \times K56 \times K57$.

The modification factor for load duration $K55$ equals

| | |
|---|---|
| Long-term loads | 1.0 |
| Medium-term loads | 1.25 |

Short-term and very short-term loads          1.50

The modification factor for moisture content $K56$ equals:

Dry timber             1.0
Green timber or timber which will be under wet
    exposure conditions         0.7
Jointed green timber which will be under dry
    exposure conditions         0.4

The modification factor $K57$ for $n$, the number of bolts in each line, equals

0.7 for $n \geq 10$, or

$$1 - \frac{3(n-1)}{100} \text{ for } n < 10$$

where $n$, the number of the same-diameter bolts acting in single or multiple shear, are symmetrically placed in one or more lines parallel to the line of action of the load in a primarily axially-loaded member in a structural framework (BS 5268: Pt 2, clause 5.11).

In all other cases where more than one bolt is used $K57 = 1.0$.

## 9.7   Toothed-plate connector joints

Toothed-plate connectors must comply with BS 1579: *Connectors for timber* and be of the sizes given in Table 70 (BS 5268: Pt 2). The bolt diameters and washer sizes are also given in Table 70. Bolt holes must be no larger than the bolt diameter plus 2 mm and the connector must not bear on the bolt threads. Both square and round washers may be used.

The bolt hole positions must be accurately set out, within 2 mm of their correct position and related to the centre-line intersection of the joining members. When drilling the bolt holes the members should be either clamped together or templates used if the members are drilled separately.

### 9.7.1   Effective cross-section

The effective cross-section is determined by deducting the net projected area of the bolt holes from the gross area of the cross-section. Any connectors and their bolts that are within 0.75 times the nominal

**134**

connector size measured parallel to the grain from a given cross-section are assumed to occur at that cross-section.

### 9.7.2  Connector spacing

The standard edge distance, end distance and spacing for each type and size of toothed-plate connector is given in Tables 71, 72 and 73 (BS 5268: Pt 2). Non-standard distances are dealt with in section 9.7.6 (BS 5268: Pt 2, clause 44.6).

For a member with its end cut at 90° to its length, the end distance is the distance from the centre of the connector to the end of the member. For ends cut at other than 90°, as shown in Figure 9.1, the end distance is the shortest distance measured along the member length, from the member end to the centre half of either:

1  for a round connector, the diameter, perpendicular to the grain, or
2  for a square connector, the width at the centre and perpendicular to the grain.

A loaded end distance or a loaded edge distance is when the force has a component acting towards the member end or the member edge.

The edge distance is measured perpendicularly from the member edge to the connector centre. If the end is not cut at 90° then the perpendicular distance from the connector centre to the sloping cut end must not be less than the edge distance.

### 9.7.3  Timber-to-timber joints

Toothed-plate connectors can generally be used with all softwoods and all hardwoods which conform to SC1 to SC5 inclusive, provided full teeth embedment can be achieved. They must be embedded prior to the insertion of the bolt by using a high-tensile steel screwed rod, with plate washers larger than the connector between the timber surfaces and the nuts at the two ends of the screwed rod. The washers should be large enough to avoid undue crushing of the timber. Before the rod is withdrawn and the permanent bolt inserted the joint should be clamped.

A connector unit is defined as one double-sided toothed-plate connector, or two single-sided toothed connectors back to back, with a bolt in single shear in a timber-to-timber joint.

### 9.7.4  Basic loads

Table 74 (BS 5268: Pt 2) gives the basic loads parallel and perpendicular to the grain. The basic loads are modified in accordance with

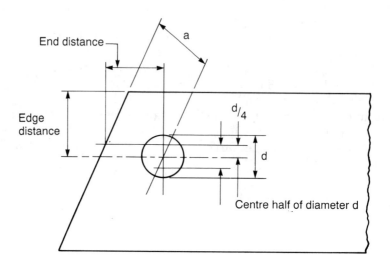

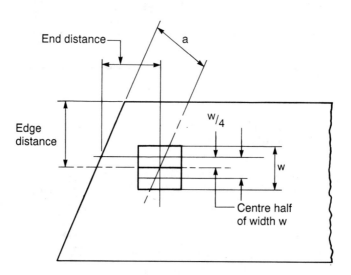

**Figure 9.1  Connector end and edge distance**

section 9.7.6 (BS 5268: Pt 2, clause 44.6) to obtain the permissible joint load. If the load is inclined at an angle $\alpha$ to the timber grain, the equation given in section 9.6.3 (clause 43.4.1) is used.

### 9.7.5 Steel plate-to-timber joints

The basic load is as given in section 9.7.4. The permissible load for a joint where there is more than one connector used with the same bolt is calculated for each connector unit and these loads should be added together for those members acting alone.

### 9.7.6 Permissible joint load

The permissible load is determined as the sum of the permissible loads for each connector unit in the joint. The permissible connector unit load is calculated as follows:

basic load $\times K58 \times K59 \times K60 \times K61$

where $K58$ is the modification factor for load duration as follows:

| | |
|---|---|
| Long-term loads | 1.0 |
| Medium-term loads | 1.12 |
| Short-term and very short-term loads | 1.25 |

$K59$ is the modification factor for moisture content as follows:

| | |
|---|---|
| Joint in dry timber | 1.0 |
| Joint in green timber or in timber which will be under wet exposure conditions. | 0.7 |
| Joint in green timber which will be under dry exposure conditions | 0.8 |

$K60$ is the modification factor for end distance, edge distance and spacing as follows:

| | |
|---|---|
| If the standard end distances, edge distances and spacings given in Tables 70, 71 and 72 are used | 1.0 |

If the end distances and/or the centre spacings are less than those given in Tables 71 and 73 then $K60$ has the lower of the $Kc$ and $Ks$ values given in Tables 75 and 73, respectively. The minimum end distances and spacings are given in Tables 71 and 73. Linear interpolation of $Kc$

and $Ks$ is allowed. If the standard end distance, edge distance or centre spacing are exceeded, no increase in load is permitted.

$K61$ is the modification factor for the number of connectors in each line as follows:

If a number ($n$) of the same-sized connectors are arranged symmetrically in one or more lines parallel to the line of action of the load in the primarily axially loaded member then

$$K61 = 1 - \frac{3(n-1)}{100} \text{ for } n < 10$$

$K61 = 0.7$ for $n \geq 10$.

For all other cases, $K61 = 1.0$.

## 9.8   Split-ring connectors

Split-ring connectors must comply with BS 1579: *Connectors for timber* and be of the size specified in Table 76 (BS 5268: Pt 2). Table 76 also gives the bolt diameter and minimum round and square washer size. Bolt holes may be up to 2 mm larger than the nominal bolt diameter.

The bolt hole positions must be accurately set out, within 2 mm of their correct position and related to the centre-line intersection of the joining members. When drilling the bolt holes the members should be either clamped together and the bolt holes drilled through all the members, or templates used if the members are drilled separately. If the members are drilled separately the split-ring grooves can be cut at the same time. Table 77 gives the dimensions of the split-ring circular grooves in the contact surfaces.

### 9.8.1   *Effective cross-section*

The effective cross-section of each member at a joint is found by deducting the projected area of the connector groove/grooves and the projected area of the portion of the bolt hole not within the projected area of the groove from the gross cross-section area.

For the multiple-connector joints, all connectors and their bolts that are within 0.75 times the connector diameter measured parallel to the grain from a given cross-section are assumed to occur at that cross-section. The effective cross-section is then found by deducting the given

138

net projected areas of the connector grooves and bolt holes from the gross cross-section area being considered.

## 9.8.2   Connector spacing

Tables 78, 79 and 80 (BS 5268: Pt 2) give the standard end distances, edge distances and spacings between connectors that allow the basic loads to apply. If the distances are less than the standard distances then the basic loads are modified as shown in section 9.8.4 (clause 45.5). The end and edge distances are those defined in section 9.7.2 (clauses 44.3.2 and 44.3.3).

## 9.8.3   Timber-to-timber joints

A connector unit is defined as one split-ring connector with a bolt in single shear.

The basic loads parallel to and perpendicular to the grain are given in Table 81 for timbers in SC1 to SC9 inclusive. Where the load is inclined to the grain of the timber, the basic load $F$ is found from section 9.6.3 (clause 43.4.1).

## 9.8.4   Permissible load for a joint

The permissible load for a joint is determined as the sum of the permissible loads for each connector unit in the joint. For more than one connector using the same bolt in a multi-member joint, the appropriate permissible load is found for each connector unit and these loads are added together for those members acting alone. Each permissible connector unit load equals:

basic load $\times K62 \times K63 \times K64 \times K65$

Where $K62$ is the load duration modification factor as follows:

Long-term load                                        1.00
Medium-term load                                    1.25
Short-term or very short-term load          1.50

$K63$ is the moisture content modification factor as follows:

Joint in dry timber                                    1.00
Joint in green timber or in timber which will be

| | |
|---|---|
| under wet exposure conditions | 0.7 |
| Joint made in green timber which will be under dry exposure conditions | 0.8 |

$K64$ is the modification factor for end distance, edge distance and spacing as follows: Tables 78, 79 and 80 give the standard end distances, edge distances and centre spacings of the connectors that allow the basic loads to apply. $K64$ is the lowest of the values of $Ks$, $Kc$, and $Kd$ given in Tables 80, 81 and 82, respectively. The distances must not be less than the minimum distances and no increase in load is permitted for distances in excess of the standard distance. If the timber is green hardwood, the standard end distance is increased by 50 per cent. The minimum end distance is half of the increased end distance with a permissible load of half of that allowed for the standard end distance.

$K65$ is the modification factor for the number of connectors in each line as follows:

If a number ($n$) of the same-sized connectors are arranged symmetrically in one or more lines parallel to the line of action of the load in the primarily axially loaded member then

$$K65 = 1 - \frac{3(n - 1)}{100} \text{ for } n < 10.$$

and $K65 = 0.7$ for $n \geq 10$

For all other cases $K65 = 1.0$.

## 9.9   Shear-plate connectors

Shear-plate connectors must comply with BS 1579: *Connectors for timber* and be of the sizes given in Table 84 (BS 5268: Pt 2). Table 84 also gives the bolt diameter and minimum round and square washer size. Bolt holes may be up to 2 mm larger than the nominal bolt diameter.

The bolt hole positions must be accurately set out, within 2 mm of their correct position and related to the centre-line intersection of the joining members. When drilling the bolt holes the members should be either clamped together and the bolt holes drilled through all the members, or templates used if the members are drilled separately. If the members are drilled separately the shear plate recesses can be cut at the same time. Figure 7 (BS 5268: Pt 2) gives the dimensions of the recesses in the contact surfaces.

### 9.9.1  Effective cross-section

The effective cross-section of each member at a joint is found by deducting the projected area of the connector recess and the projected area of the bolt hole not within the projected area of the recess from the gross cross-section area. The connector recess depths are 11.5 and 16.5 mm for the 67 and the 102 mm shear plates, respectively.

For multiple-connector joints all connectors and their bolts that are within 0.75 times the connector diameter measured parallel to the grain from a given cross-section are assumed to occur at that cross-section. The effective cross-section is then found by deducting the given net projected areas of the connector grooves and bolt holes from the gross cross-section area being considered.

### 9.9.2  Connector spacing

Tables 78, 79 and 80 (BS 5268: Pt 2) give the standard end distances, edge distances and spacings between each size of connector that allow the basic loads to apply. If the distances are less than the standard distances then the basic loads are modified as shown in section 9.9.5 (clause 46.6). The end and edge distances are those defined in section 9.7.2 (clauses 44.3.2 and 44.3.3).

### 9.9.3  Timber-to-timber joints

A connector consists of two shear plates, used back-to-back with the bolt in single shear. All chips and shavings are to be removed from the recess. The basic loads parallel to and perpendicular to the grain are given in Table 85 (BS 5268: Pt 2) for timbers in SC1 to SC9 inclusive. Where the load is inclined to the grain of the timber, the basic load $F$ is found from section 9.6.3 (clause 43.4.1).

### 9.9.4  Steel plate-to-timber joints

The steel plates must have adequate strength and be designed to BS 449: Pt 2. The basic load is found from section 9.9.3.

### 9.9.5  Permissible load for a joint

The permissible load for a joint is determined as the sum of the permissible loads for each connector unit in the joint. For more than one connector using the same bolt in a multi-member joint, the appropriate permissible load is found for each connector unit and these loads are added together for those members acting alone. Table 86 (BS 5268: Pt 2) gives the limiting values for the permissible loads of a connector unit. Each permissible connector unit load equals:

basic load $\times$ $K66$ $\times$ $K67$ $\times$ $K68$ $\times$ $K69$

where $K66$ is the load duration modification factor as follows:

| | |
|---|---|
| Long-term load | 1.00 |
| Medium-term load | 1.25 |
| Short-term or very short-term load | 1.50 |

$K67$ is the moisture content modification factor as follows:

| | |
|---|---|
| Joint in dry timber | 1.00 |
| Joint in green timber or in timber which will be under wet exposure conditions | 0.7 |
| Joint made in green timber which will be under dry exposure conditions | 0.8 |

$K68$ is the modification factor for end distance, edge distance and centre spacing as follows:

Tables 78, 79 and 80 (BS 5268: Pt 2) give the standard end distances, edge distances and centre spacings of the connectors that allow the basic loads to apply. $K68$ is the lowest of the values of $Ks$, $Kc$, and $Kd$ given in Tables 80, 81 and 82, respectively, for distances less than the standard distances. The distances must not be less than the minimum distances and no increase in load is permitted for distances in excess of the standard distance.

If the timber is green hardwood, the standard end distance is increased by 50 per cent. The minimum end distance is half of the increased end distance with a permissible load of half of that allowed for the standard end distance.

$K69$ is the modification factor for the number of connectors in each line as follows:

If a number $(n)$ of the same-sized connectors are arranged symmetrically in one or more lines parallel to the line of action of the load in the primarily axially-loaded member then

$$K69 = 1 - \frac{3(n-1)}{100} \text{ for } n < 10.$$

and $K69 = 0.7$ for $n \geq 10$

For all other cases for more than one connector $K69 = 1.0$.

## 9.10 Glued joints

*9.10.1 Laterally-loaded joints*

Joints in structural components made from timber, plywood, tempered hardboard or wood chipboard that are fastened together with glue should be manufactured in accordance to BS 6446.

The timber, except excessively resinous pieces, must be one of the softwoods listed in Table 92 of Appendix A (BS 5268: Pt 2), plywoods listed in Chapter 7 (BS 5268: Pt 2, clauses 24 to 30) and tempered hardboard in Chapter 8 (clause 34). For the gluing of resinous softwoods and for all hardwoods, the glue manufacturer's advice is required.

Only the following structural joints are covered:

1   Between solid or laminated timber members whose dimensions at right-angles to the plane of the glue line is not greater than 50 mm.
2   Between solid or laminated timber members of any dimension and plywood not greater than 29 mm in thickness.
3   Between solid or laminated timber members of any dimension and tempered hardboard not greater than 8 mm in thickness.
4   Between plywood members of any thickness.
5   Between tempered hardboard members of any thickness.

Mechanical fasteners, when present in a glued joint, should not be considered as contributing to the joint strength. However, if bonding pressure is generated by nails or staples, the permissible shear stress for the glue line should be multiplied by the nail/glue modification factor $K70 = 0.9$.

Table 87 (BS 5268: Pt 2) lists the four exposure categories, together with the permitted adhesives. The glue must be appropriate to the environment in which the joint will be used. In the case of MR-type adhesives to BS 1204: *Synthetic resin adhesives for wood* the formulation used must be suitable for the service conditions and the intended life of the structure.

*9.10.2 Timber-to-timber joints*

Eccentric glued lap joints which induce tension perpendicular to the plane of the glue line are not permitted.

The permissible shear stress for adhesives in lap joints where the joint components are loaded parallel to the grain is the lesser of the permissible shear stresses parallel to the grain. If one face of the joint is loaded at an angle to the grain, the permissible shear stress for the glue line is:

$$\tau_\alpha = \tau_{adm,\parallel} \, (1 - 0.67 \sin \alpha)$$

where $\alpha$ is the angle between the load direction and the longitudinal axis and $\tau_{adm,\parallel}$ is the permissible shear stress parallel to the grain stress for the timber.

### 9.10.3 Timber-to-plywood, tempered hardboard or wood chipboard joints

The permissible shear stress for a joint loaded parallel to the grain is taken as the permissible shear parallel to the grain for the timber, or the appropriate rolling shear stress for the plywood, tempered hardboard or wood chipboard, whichever has the lower value. If the timber is loaded at an angle to the grain the equation given in section 9.10.2 (BS 5268: Pt 2, clause 47.1.3) applies. The rolling stress for plywood, tempered hardboard or wood chipboard is independent of the load direction within the plane of the board.

### 9.10.4 Plywood-to-plywood, tempered hardboard-to-tempered hardboard and chipboard-to-chipboard joints

The permissible shear stress for a joint is the appropriate rolling shear stress for the plywood, tempered hardboard, or wood chipboard.

### 9.10.5 Finger joints

Finger joints should be manufactured to and have a joint efficiency in accordance with BS 5291: *Finger joints in structural softwoods*. The efficiency rating should not be less than that required for the grade of timber, unless the permissible stress is reduced accordingly. The efficiency ratings of some common finger profiles are given in Appendix F (BS 5268: Pt 2), but in no case should the rating be less than 50 per cent. Finger joint efficiencies for compression parallel to the grain are given in Table 104.

Finger joints may be used in load-sharing systems, but they should not be used in principal members, load-sharing systems or members acting alone where the failure of any single joint could lead to collapse. Finger joints may be used in:

1 laterally interconnected members;
2 timber members in components built up from pieces of timber, or timber and plywood or tempered hardboard in which bending or tension stresses are resisted by at least two pieces of equally-strained interconnected timber.

The usual design requirements, however, must be met and if any one finger joint is removed, the member must continue to support without collapse the combined full dead load, plant load, machinery or storage loads and at least one-third of other imposed loads and wind loads.

The remaining structure or member may have a stress value of twice the permissible stress values for the strength class or species and grade used in the initial design. The duration of load factor $K3$ is 1.0 irrespective of the types of load being considered.

The suitability of finger joints in hardwoods should be determined by test, and supplemented as necessary by additional tests for tension parallel to the grain. The suitability and long-term durability of the adhesives used for the particular hardwood species and exposure conditions must also be checked.

Finger joints do not affect the modulus of elasticity and the full cross-section may be used in calculations.

## 9.11 Design example 1: Nailed timber-to-timber joint

*A nailed timber joint is required to sustain a medium-term axial load of 6 kN. The timber is a softwood of SC4 and sized 50 × 146 mm. Determine the number of nails and their spacings if 4 mm, 90 mm-long round wire nails are to be used.*

For 4 mm diameter nails, the standard headside and pointside member thicknesses are 32 and 44 mm, respectively. Pre-drilling of the holes is not usual in a SC4 softwood. Both of the required thicknesses are less than the member thickness of 50 mm, and the full basic shear loads given in Table 59 (BS 5268: Pt 2) may be used provided the nails are long enough. The 90 mm-long nail will penetrate the 50 mm-thick headside member and 40 mm into the pointside member. The 40 mm penetration is 4 mm less than the 44 mm penetration required in Table 59.

From Table 59, the basic single shear lateral load for round wire nails driven at right-angles to the grain into SC4 timber is 405 N. The basic load must be reduced in accordance with section 9.4.3 (BS 5268: Pt 2, clause 41.4) as follows:

$$405 \text{ N} \times \frac{\text{(actual pointside penetration)}}{\text{(standard pointside penetration)}} = 368.18 \text{ N}$$

The permissible load per nail (section 9.4.7 (clause 41.8)) is found as follows:

basic load $\times$ $K48$ $\times$ $K49$ $\times$ $K50$

where $K48 = 1.12$ for the medium-term load, $K49 = 1.0$ for a joint in dry timber, and $K50 = 1.0$, as it is assumed that there will be less than 10 nails of the same diameter in each line of nails symmetrically arranged in lines parallel to the line of action of the load, giving

permissible load per nail = 368.18 N $\times$ 1.12 $\times$ 1.0 $\times$ 1.0 = 412.36 N.

The required number of nails

$$= \frac{\text{Total load}}{\text{Permissible load per nail}} = \frac{6 \text{ kN}}{412.36 \text{ N}} = 14.55$$

Rounded to the nearest whole number above, 14.55 gives 15 nails. The nails could be in three lines of five nails or four lines of four nails. For this example, four lines of four nails will be used, as shown in Figure 9.2.

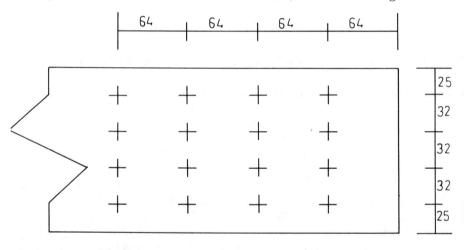

**Figure 9.2   Minimum nail spacing**

The minimum nail spacing is given in Table 58. Provided the timber is a softwood other than Douglas fir, the nail spacings in a timber-to-timber joint may be multiplied by 0.8. The edge distance must not be less than five nail diameters.

End distance parallel to the grain    = 20 $\times$ 4.0 mm $\times$ 0.8 = 64 mm

Edge distance perpendicular to the
grain     = 5 × 4.0 mm = 20 mm

Distance between lines of nails
perpendicular to the grain     = 10 × 4.0 mm × 0.8 = 32 mm

Distance between adjacent nails in
any one line, parallel to the grain     = 20 × 4.0 mm × 0.8 = 64 mm

The locations of the distances 64 mm, 32 mm and 25 mm are as shown in Figure 9.2.

It must be remembered that in some designs of nailed joints, the timber stress in the effective cross-section may require checking section 9.4.1 (clause 41.2).

## 9.12 Design example 2: Screwed steel plate-to-timber joint

*An SC4 softwood member carries an axial medium-term load of 4.8 kN. The load will be transferred to a steel plate 4 mm thick which will be screwed to the side of the timber and have adequate strength to sustain the load. Determine the countersunk screw size, hole size and minimum timber width, if the joint will be in dry timber 38 mm thick.*

The screws will be loaded in single shear and be inserted through the steel plate at right-angles into the side grain of the timber. The total combined thickness of the steel plate (4 mm) and the timber (38 mm) is 42 mm, which limits the screw length to 42 mm. Screws are usually used in preference to nails where the penetration depth is restricted.

Using Table 65 (BS 5268: Pt 2), only screws of diameter 3.45, 4.17 and 4.88 mm have a pointside penetration depth of less than the timber thickness of 38 mm. As the holes will be pre-drilled, the minimum number of the largest diameter screws will be used, namely 4.88 mm, 38 mm long. The pre-drilled hole in the steel plate will be 4.88 mm diameter and the pilot hole in the timber (section 9.5 (BS 5268: Pt 2, clause 42.1)) will be 0.4 times the shank diameter of 4.88 mm, namely 2 mm. The steel plate must be countersunk to accommodate the screws.

Using Table 65, the basic single shear lateral load for a 4.88 mm diameter screw inserted at right-angles to the grain into a SC4 softwood is 445 N. As the steel plate has adequate strength, the basic load is multiplied by the steel-to-timber modification factor $K46$ (section 9.5.6 (clause 42.5.2)), which has a value of 1.25 giving a basic load of:

$$445 \text{ N} \times 1.25(K46) = 556.25 \text{ N.}$$

The permissible screw load = basic load × $K52$ × $K53$ × $K54$,

where basic load = 556.25 N, $K52$ = 1.12 the duration of load factor, $K53$ = 1.0 the moisture content modification factor for dry timber, and $K54$ = 1.0 as there will be only one line of less than ten screws, giving a permissible load of

556.25 N × 1.12($K52$) × 1.0($K53$) × 1.0($K54$) = 623 N.

The required number of nails

$$= \frac{\text{Total axial load}}{623\text{ N}} = \frac{4800\text{ N}}{623\text{ N}} = 7.7.$$

Therefore use eight screws in two lines of four.
The minimum nail spacing is given in Table 64 as follows, rounded to the nearest whole number above:

End distance parallel to the grain     = 10 × 4.88 mm = 49 mm
Edge distance perpendicular to the
  grain                              = 5 × 4.88 mm = 25 mm
Distance between lines of screws,
  perpendicular to the grain     = 3 × 4.88 mm = 15 mm
Distance between adjacent screws in
  any one line, parallel to the grain     = 10 × 4.88 mm = 49 mm

The location of the distances 49 mm, 25 mm, and 15 mm are as shown in Figure 9.3.

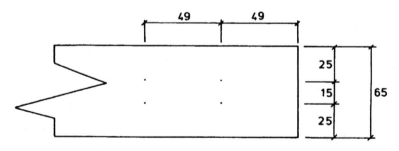

**Figure 9.3   Minimum screw spacing and timber size**

It must be remembered that in some designs of screwed joints, the timber stress in the effective cross-section may require checking (see section 9.5.1 (clause 42.2)).

## 9.13   Design example 3: Timber-to-timber bolted joint

*A horizontal beam carries a medium-term load of 2.3 kN. The beam is supported from above by two vertical members in tension. All three members are SC4 softwoods. Determine the minimum timber dimensions if the vertical members are to be secured to the horizontal member using M12 black bolts in single shear in a two-member joint. The joint is to be dry timber. Figure 9.4 shows the arrangement of one of the two joints.*

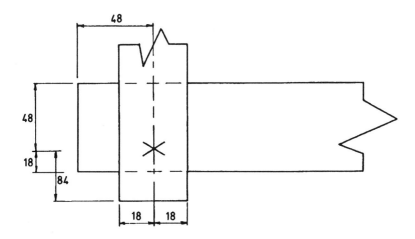

**Figure 9.4   Minimum timber size and bolt positions**

Using M12 black bolts, the nominal washer diameter and thickness are $3 \times 12$ mm diameter = 36 mm and $0.25 \times 12$ mm diameter = 3 mm respectively (see section 9.6 (BS 5268: Pt 2, clause 43.1)). The maximum bolt hole diameter in the timber is 12 mm + 2 mm = 14 mm.

*Permissible load*

The permissible load (see section 9.6.6 (clause 43.6)) = basic load $\times$ $K55 \times K56 \times K57$,

where $K55 = 1.25$ the medium-term load (duration of load modification factor), $K56 = 1.0$ the moisture content modification factor for a dry joint, and $K57 = 1.0$ as there is only one bolt in each joint, giving

the permissible load = basic load $\times 1.25 \times 1.0 \times 1.0$.

The load carried by each bolt = 2.3 kN ÷ 2 bolts = 1.15 kN and must be less than the permissible load per bolt which is 1.25 times the basic load. If the applied load equals the permissible load then the basic load equals 1.15 kN ÷ 1.25 = 0.92 kN. Usually the applied load is less than the permissible load and the basic load of 0.92 kN is the minimum basic load.

Using Table 69 (BS 5268: Pt 2), with an M12 bolt and SC4 timber, the basic shear load for one bolt loaded parallel to the grain for a 16 mm-thick thinner member is 1.07 kN. The permissible load is 1.07 kN × 1.25($K55$) = 1.34 kN.

For the basic shear load for one bolt loaded perpendicularly to the grain, Table 69 gives for a thinner member of 25 mm a basic load of 0.929 kN. The permissible load is 0.929 kN × 1.25($K55$) = 1.16 kN.

Where the members of unequal thickness are joined at an angle, in this case 90°, the basic load for the smaller member should be used. However, the two thicknesses of 16 and 25 mm are the minimum that can be used for the vertical and horizontal members, respectively. Consequently, both members will be made of the same thicker size, namely 25 mm.

The bolt spacing (section 9.6.2 (clause 43.3)) is as follows:

There is only one bolt in each joint and the spacing between bolts is not required. For loading bearing parallel to the grain and towards the end of the timber, the minimum end distance is 7 × 12 mm diameter = 84 mm and 4 × 12  m = 48 mm when loaded away from the end.

The distance from the edge of the timber to the centre of the bolt hole is 1.5 × 12 mm diameter = 18 mm, but for loading perpendicular to the grain, the distance from the timber edge towards which the bolt is bearing to the bolt centre = 4 × 12 mm diameter = 48 mm.

## 9.14   Design example 4: Toothed-plate connector joint

*Two round, double-sided, toothed-plate connectors of nominal size 51 mm are to be used to join together two members carrying an axial medium-term tensile load of 9.5 kN. If the members are 50 mm × 150 mm and are of SC5 hardwood, determine if both the toothed-plate connector and the timber size are adequate.*

The SC5 hardwood may only be used provided full embedment of the teeth can be achieved. The connector will be embedded prior to the insertion of the bolt. For a 51 mm nominal size connector, the bolt hole maximum diameter is 14 mm (12 mm diameter + 2 mm) and the minimum round washer diameter and thickness are 38 and 3 mm, respectively (BS 5268: Pt 2, Table 68).

The basic load for one toothed-plate connector loaded parallel to the grain is found from Table 74. The member thickness on both sides of the 51 mm nominal-sized double-sided connector is 50 mm. For SC5 timber the basic load parallel to the grain is 4.53 kN.

The permissible load (section 9.7.6 (BS 5268: Pt 2, clause 44.6)) is

basic load 4.53 kN × $K58$ × $K59$ × $K60$ × $K61$

where $K58 = 1.12$ the medium-term load duration factor, $K59 = 1.0$ the joint in dry timber moisture content modification factor, $K60 = 1.0$ as the standard end, edge and spacing distances will be used, and

$$K61 = 1 - \frac{3(n-1)}{100} = 0.97$$

where $n = 2$, the number of the same-sized connector units arranged in one line parallel to the line of action, giving

permissible load = 4.53 kN × 1.12 × 1.0 × 1.0 × 0.97 = 4.92 kN.

For two connectors the permissible total load of 9.84 kN (2 × 4.92 kN) is greater than the applied load of 9.5 kN and is satisfactory.

The standard end distance, edge distance and connector spacings which allow the basic load to be used for the 51 mm round toothed-plate connector are given in Tables 71, 72 and 73 (section 9.7.2 (clause 44.3.1)) and are as follows:

| | |
|---|---:|
| Unloaded end distance, loaded parallel to the grain | 38 mm |
| Loaded end distance, loaded parallel to the grain | 89 mm |
| Unloaded and loaded edge distance | 32 mm |
| The spacing depends upon: 1, the angle of the load to the grain, and 2, the angle between the centres of the two connectors and the grain, which again is zero degrees as the connectors are in line along the grain. The spacing is | 76 mm |

As the end distance, edge distance and the connector spacing will not be less than the standard values and the ends of the two members are to be cut at right-angles to the member length, no modification of $K60$ is required (section 9.7.6 (clause 44.6)). Figure 9.5 gives the standard distances and spacings. Although the timber width of 150 mm allows a greater edge distance than the standard distance, no increase in loading is permitted.

**151**

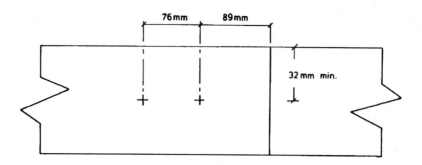

**Figure 9.5   Standard end distance, edge distance and spacings**

## 9.15   Design example 5: Split-ring connector joint

*Two 102 mm diameter split-ring connectors are to be used to transfer a load in a dry SC4 timber-to-timber joint. The timber thickness on both sides of the connector is 63 mm. Determine the maximum medium-term load the joint can sustain if one timber member is loaded parallel to the grain and the other timber member is loaded perpendicular to the grain. The standard end distance, edge distance and spacing between connectors is to be used to permit the basic loads to apply. The ends of the members are square cut (section 9.7.6 (BS 5268: Pt 2, clause 44.3.2)).*

The standard end distance, edge distance and connector spacing are found in Tables 78, 79 and 80 (BS 5268: Pt 2), respectively, as follows:

| | |
|---|---|
| Unloaded end distance, loaded parallel to the grain | 140 mm |
| Loaded end distance, loaded parallel to the grain | 178 mm |

As the example does not state whether the loaded or unloaded distance is required, the largest end distance of 178 mm is used for the vertical member shown in Figure 9.6.

For the vertical member, the unloaded edge distance, loaded parallel to the grain is required (Table 79): 70 mm.

For the horizontal member, the load is applied perpendicular to the grain, but it is not stated whether the edge is loaded or unloaded. For this reason the loaded edge distance, loaded perpendicular to the grain is required (Table 79): 95 mm.

The connector spacing depends upon:

1  The angle of the load to the grain, and
2  the angle between the centres of the two connectors and the grain.

For the vertical member, the load is at 90° to the grain and the angle

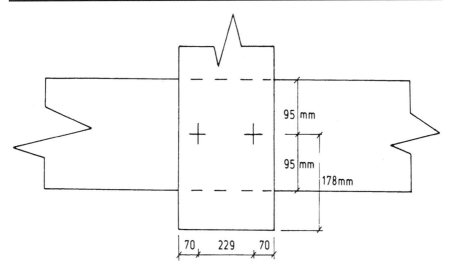

**Figure 9.6  Standard end, edge and spacing distances – split-ring connector and shear-plate connector**

between the centres of the two connectors and the grain is 90° giving a spacing of 165 mm.

For the horizontal member, both the load and the connectors are in line with the grain and from Table 80 the spacing is found to be 229 mm, which is greater than the 165 mm found for the vertical member. As the spacings in both members must be the same, the spacing of 229 mm is used.

Tables 76 and 77 show that for a 102 mm nominal-sized split-ring connector an M20 bolt is required with a minimum size of round or square washer of 75 mm diameter or side length, being 5 mm thick. The circular grooves in the timber are 5.3 mm wide, 12.7 mm deep, with an inside diameter of 104 mm. The bolt-hole diameter must be between 20 and 22 mm (section 9.8 (clause 45.1.2)).

It may be necessary to check the effective cross-section if the end, edge and spacing distances are less than the standard (section 9.8.1 (clause 45.2)).

The permissible connector unit load

$$= \text{basic load} \times K62 \times K63 \times K64 \times K65,$$

where the basic load is given in Table 81, which for the SC4 timber, 63 mm thick, and the 102 mm split-ring connector, is 15.4 kN parallel to the grain and 10.8 kN perpendicular to the grain. The lower of the two values is the limiting basic load, namely 10.8 kN.

$K62 = 1.25$ the medium-term duration of load modification factor, $K63 = 1.0$ the dry timber moisture content modification factor, $K64 = 1.0$ the modification factor for where the end, edge and spacing distances are less than the standard values, and $K65 = 1.0$ the modification factor for the number of connectors in a line in the primarily axially-loaded vertical member, giving

permissible connector unit load = 10.8 kN (basic load) $\times$ 1.25($K62$) $\times$ 1.0($K63$) $\times$ 1.0($K64$) $\times$ 1.0($K65$) = 13.5 kN.

The permissible load in the two split-ring connector joint = 2 $\times$ 13.5 kN = 27 kN.

## 9.16   Design example 6: Shear-plate connector joint

*Two 102 mm diameter shear-plate connectors are to be used to transfer a load in a dry SC4 timber-to-timber joint. The timber thickness on both sides of the connector is 63 mm. Determine the maximum medium-term load the joint can sustain if one timber member is loaded parallel to the grain and the other timber member is loaded perpendicular to the grain. The standard end distance, edge distance and spacing between connectors is to be used to permit the basic loads to apply. The ends of the members are square cut (section 9.7.2 (BS 5268: Pt 2, clauses 44.3.2 and 44.3.3)).*

The standard end distance, edge distance and connector spacing are found from Tables 78, 79 and 80 (BS 5268: Pt 2), respectively, as follows:

Unloaded end distance, loaded parallel to the grain          140 mm
Loaded end distance, loaded parallel to the grain            178 mm

As the example does not state whether the loaded or unloaded distance is required, the largest end distance of 178 mm is used for the vertical member shown in Figure 9.6.

For the vertical member, the unloaded edge distance, loaded parallel to the grain is required (Table 79): 70 mm.

For the horizontal member, the load is applied perpendicular to the grain, but it is not stated whether the edge is loaded or unloaded. For this reason the loaded edge distance, loaded perpendicular to the grain is required (Table 79): 95 mm.

The connector spacing depends upon:

1   the angle of the load to the grain, and
2   the angle between the centres of the two connectors and the grain.

For the vertical member, the load is at 90° to the grain and the angle between the centres of the two connectors and the grain is 90°, giving a spacing of 165 mm.

For the horizontal member, both the load and the connectors are in line with the grain and from Table 80 the spacing is found to be 229 mm, which is greater than the 165 mm found for the vertical member. As the spacings in both members must be the same, the spacing of 229 mm is used.

Table 84 shows that for a 102 mm nominal-sized shear-plate connector an M20 bolt is required with a minimum size of round or square washer of 75 mm diameter or side length, being 5 mm thick. Figure 7 of BS 5268: Pt 2 shows the dimensions of the circular recesses in the timber members for the 102 mm connector unit. The bolt-hole diameter must be between 20 and 22 mm (section 9.9 (clause 46.1.2)).

It may be necessary to check the effective cross-section if the end, edge and spacing distances are less than the standard (section 9.9.1 (clause 46.2)).

The permissible shear-plate connector unit load

$$= \text{basic load} \times K66 \times K67 \times K68 \times K69,$$

where the basic load for one shear-plate connector unit is given in Table 85, which for the SC4 timber, 63 mm thick, and the 102 mm connector, is 12.1 kN parallel to the grain and 8.47 kN perpendicular to the grain. The lower of the two values is the limiting basic load, namely 8.47 kN.

$K66 = 1.25$ the medium-term duration of load modification factor, $K67 = 1.0$ the dry timber moisture content modification factor, $K68 = 1.0$ the modification factor for where the end, edge and spacing distances are less than the standard values, and $K69 = 1.0$ the modification factor for the number of connectors in a line in the primarily axially-loaded vertical member, giving

permissible connector unit load $= 8.47$ kN (basic load) $\times 1.25(K66) \times 1.0(K67) \times 1.0(K68) \times 1.0(K69) = 10.59$ kN.

The permissible load in the shear-plate connector joint $= 2 \times 10.59$ kN $= 21.18$ kN.

Figure 9.6 shows the standard end, edge and spacing distances, which are the same as for the split-ring connector.

# 10   Timber treatments

## 10.1   Introduction

It is not intended in this book to delve into the details of timber treatments. Readers are advised to refer to BS 5268: Pt 5: 1977, *Preservative treatments for constructional timber* and to the publications of timber treatment manufacturers. BS 5268: Pt 5 gives advice on the design, treatment and properties of treated timber.

All timber treatments must be compatible with the timber, the metal fasteners and adhesives such that they do not adversely affect the satisfactory performance and structural integrity throughout the intended life of the structure. Any timber that is cut or sawn after treatment must be given the appropriate treatment before assembly.

## 10.2   Adhesives

Special precautions may be necessary when gluing timbers treated with wood preservatives or flame retardants, to ensure their compatibility.

## 10.3   Anti-corrosive treatments

The anti-corrosive treatments applied to the metal fasteners and fittings must not adversely affect the joint strength throughout the intended life of the structure.

## 10.4  Decorative treatments

Where timber has been painted, varnished or otherwise decorated, the work must be in accordance with BS 6150, *Code of Practice for painting of buildings* and care taken to ensure that the paints, preservatives, flame retardants and adhesives are compatible.

## 10.5  Flame-retardant treatments

Flame retardants can adversely affect metallic fittings and reduce joint strength. Timber so treated should not be freely exposed to the weather or environmental conditions that will affect the performance of the treatment.

## 10.6  Preservative treatments

Where preservative treatment is required it should comply with BS 5268: Pt 5: 1977 and not adversely affect the strength of the metal or glued joints over the intended life of the structure. The moisture content of treated timber at its assembly stage should be monitored.

The preservative treatment of trussed rafters, other than in those areas specified in the building regulations, may be regarded as unnecessary as the risk of rot or insect attack in well-ventilated pitched roofs is regarded by BS 5268: Pt 2 as low.

# 11  Fire resistance

## 11.1  Introduction

The determination of the fire resistance of timber members is found in BS 5268: Pt 4: 1978, Section 4.1, 'Recommendations for calculating fire resistance of timber members'. It gives recommendations for assessing the fire resistance of flexural tension and compression members of solid or glued laminated timber and their joints and is described in this chapter.

## 11.2  Behaviour of timber in fire

Timber is assumed to char at its surface at a steady rate, with the uncharred timber not losing any significant strength. It is possible, therefore, to predict the fire resistance performance of certain flexural, tension and compression members. The notional rates of charring for calculating the residual section are given in Table 11.1. The residual section is the section of uncharred timber left after a given period of exposure to fire, and having taken into account any accelerated charring at exposed arrises.

The charring rates of Table 11.1 also apply to glued laminated members and finger joints manufactured to BS 5291 provided certain thermosetting phenolic and aminoplastic synthetic resin adhesives are used.

**Table 11.1  Notional charring rates (mm)**

| Species | Charring in 30 min | Charring in 60 min |
|---|---|---|
| (a) All structural species listed in Appendix A of BS 5268: Pt 2: 1991, except (b) and (c) below | 20 | 40 |
| (b) Western red cedar | 25 | 50 |
| (C) Hardwoods having a normal density not less than 650 kg/m$^3$ at 18% m.c. | 15 | 30 |

Note: Linear interpolation is allowed for periods between 15 and 90 minutes
Source: Reproduced with permission from BS 5268: Section 4.1

Sections built up with metal fasteners must have the metal fasteners fully protected from the effects of the fire for the charring rates of Table 11.1 to apply.

## 11.3  Accelerated rates of charring

Arrises become increasingly rounded during exposure to fire and the radius of this rounding is equal to the depth of charring, with its centre equidistant from the two faces at a distance of twice the charring depth, as shown in Figure 11.1. If the exposure to the fire is less than 30 minutes and the least dimension of the rectangular residual section is not less than 50 mm, rounding may be disregarded.

## 11.4  Stability considerations

In the context of fire resistance, stability is defined as the ability to sustain the applied load throughout the period of the exposure to fire, which applies to tension members, compression members such as columns, and to flexural members. In the case of flexural members there is the additional requirement of the ability to restrict deflection to the span divided by 20.

If the members form part of a fire-resisting construction, the insulation and integrity requirements may also be applicable.

**159**

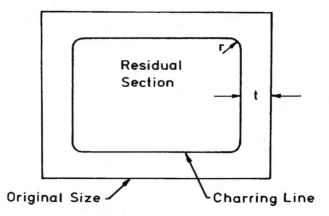

**Figure 11.1   Calculating the radius of the arris**

## 11.5   Flexural members

The residual section should be able to support either the maximum permissible design load or the load based on those which the member is required to support in normal service. The deflection under the appropriate design load should not exceed the span divided by 20. Due to this large deflection limit the stability and integrity of other parts of the structure may have to be considered.

The residual section is the original section less the amount of charring related to Table 11.1 and the period of fire resistance.

The flexural load-bearing capacity is calculated in the usual way using the residual section and stresses of 2.25 times the permissible long-term dry stresses if the minimum initial breadth of the section is 70 mm or more. If the minimum initial breadth is less than 70 mm, the 2.25 becomes 2.00.

The deflection is calculated using the residual section and the dry value of the mean or minimum modulus of elasticity as used in the original design.

## 11.6   Compression members

The residual section should be able to support either the maximum design compressive load or the loads based on those which the member is required to support in normal service.

If the column is exposed to fire on all faces, the charring rate of each face is 1.25 times the rates of Table 11.1.

When the column abuts or forms part of a wall which provides fire resistance, charring on all the column faces is unlikely. The charring calculations are then based on the area of column on the side of the wall that has the greatest surface exposure. The junction between the column and the wall must be a fire barrier.

If the column is part of a wall, or abuts a wall, where fire resistance is required on one side of the wall only, the charring of the column faces exposed to the fire need only be considered.

In determining the effective length of the residual column section, only the positional end restraints are considered to act, unless the residual joint shows some degree of directional restraint. The residual section slenderness ratio should not exceed 250 and the stress modification factor for long-term loads must be derived from Table 20 of BS 5268: Pt 2.

The strength of the residual section should be calculated using the compressive stress parallel to the grain of two times the permissible long-term dry stress.

The strength of the compressive member subjected to bending should be calculated in accordance with section 4.6 (BS 5268: Pt 2, clause 15.6) using the above calculated stresses in place of the permissible stress.

## 11.7 Tension members

To determine the load-bearing capacity of tension members, the charring rates of Table 11.1 are multiplied by 1.25, and the long-term dry stresses by 2.

If the tension member is also subjected to bending, the strength is calculated in accordance with section 5.8 (BS 5268: Pt 2, clause 16.3) and the information given in this chapter.

## 11.8 Joints

The charring rates of Table 11.1 apply in all cases when faces of the abutting pieces of timber are held in close contact and where special attention is paid to the placement or protection of metal components and fasteners, as the junctions between members are vulnerable to fire effects. If compressive forces are transmitted by direct timber-to-timber bearing, the loss of strength will be small, but for other types of joint that transfer forces between members an assessment must be made of the residual timber, paying particular attention to the effects of any metal parts.

In redundant structures, the relative stiffness may alter and redistribute the forces, necessitating a further structural analysis.

## 11.9   Metal fasteners

All metal exposed on the surface of a timber member will act as a heat sink and lead to localized charring. Metal fasteners must be placed so that they are within the residual section, with all holes being securely timber plugged and glued. Alternatively, the exposed part of the fastener can be covered with timber, plasterboard, insulating board or equivalent that will stay in position for the required fire resistance time.

Steel hangers for joists or beams must be protected by the ceiling members or locally with a protecting material.

The metal plates and other metal connectors can be used without restriction in trussed rafter construction when no fire resistance requirements exist. If protection is necessary, the requirements of the first paragraph of this section are used.

## 11.10   Design example 1: The residual section strength of a roof beam

*An SC3 timber roof beam is to have 30 minutes fire resistance. If the initial beam size is 100 × 195 mm, as shown in Figure 11.2, determine the residual section size, the permissible stresses, and the maximum allowable deflection, if the span is 8 metres.*

As the beam is a roof beam, the upper edge will be protected from the fire and only the three lower faces will be subjected to fire.

The SC3 timber is not specified by species, but using Table 3 of BS 5268: Pt 2 and comparing it with Table 11.1 and Appendix A of BS 5268: Pt 2, all SC3 timbers are designated (a) of Table 11.1 with a charring rate of 20 mm in 30 minutes. The size of the residual section is 175 mm (195 − 20) by 60 mm (100 − 20 − 20), as shown in Figure 11.3. The rounding of the arrises is not taken into account as the period of fire exposure does not exceed 30 minutes and the minimum residual section is 60 mm.

The minimum initial breadth is greater than 70 mm (section 11.5) and the permissible stress is

$2.25 \times 5.3$ N/mm$^2$ (Table 8) $\times 1.061$ $K7$(depth factor) $= 12.653$ N/mm$^2$.

The maximum permissible deflection $= 8000$ mm/20 $= 400$ mm.

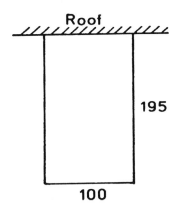

Figure 11.2 Section through
roof beam and
roof

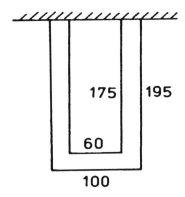

Figure 11.3 Residual section
size

## 11.11 Design example 2: The fire resistance of a hardwood column

*An SC9 hardwood column, 100 × 150 mm is subjected to fire on all four sides for 30 minutes. Determine the size of the residual section, the maximum column length, and the permissible compressive stress.*

Table 8 of BS 5268: Pt 2 lists only greenheart as an SC9 timber, and using Table 11.1 a charring rate of 15 mm in 30 minutes is given. Greenheart has a normal density in excess of 650 kg/m³. As the column has four faces exposed to fire, the charring rate is multiplied by 1.25 (section 11.6) to 18.75 mm per 30 minutes. The residual timber size is 112.5 mm (150 − 18.75 − 18.75) by 62.5 mm (100 − 18.75 − 18.75), as shown in Figure 11.4. The rounding of the arris is not considered (section 11.3).

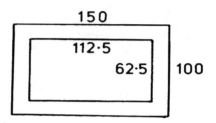

**Figure 11.4  Column section and residual section**

The maximum slenderness ratio is 250, with only the end positional restraint assumed to act, giving the ratio of effective length to actual length as 1 (Table 21). Therefore, $L_e/i = 250$.

The radius of gyration $i$ is found from the least value of $I$, where $I = bd^3/12$.

$$I = \frac{112.5 \text{ mm} \times 62.5^3}{12} = 2.288 \times 10^6 \text{ mm}^4$$

but $I = b \times d \times i^2$ giving

$$i^2 = \frac{2.288 \times 10^6 \text{ mm}^4}{112.5 \text{ mm} \times 62.5 \text{ mm}}$$

$$\therefore i = 18.042 \text{ mm}$$

and a maximum length of 18.042 mm × 250 = 4511 mm.

The compressive stress parallel to the grain is found from

$2.00 \times$ the permissible long-term dry stress $= 19.5 \text{ N/mm}^2$ (Table 8) $\times K12$ (Table 22) $= 39.0 \text{ N/mm}^2 \times K12$;

where $K12$ is found from Table 22 using the value of the slenderness ratio and $E/\sigma_{c,\parallel}$.

If the compression member is also subjected to bending, then clause 15.6 of BS 5268: Pt 2 is used and the permissible stresses are derived as shown in this and the previous design example

## 11.12 Design example 3: A tension member subject to fire

*A tension member of SC2, SS grade western red cedar, has a section size of 150 × 150 mm and is to have 30 minutes fire resistance. Determine its residual section and the permissible stresses if the section is also subjected to bending.*

Western red cedar has a charring rate of 25 mm in 30 minutes which is multiplied by 1.25 (section 11.7) giving a charring rate of 31.75 mm per 30 minutes and a final size of 87.5 (150 − 31.25 − 31.25) × 87.5 mm. The rounding of the arris need not be considered (section 11.3).

The permissible stress of 2.00 times the permissible long-term dry stress, which for SS grade western red cedar is higher than the SC2 values, gives

$$
\begin{aligned}
\text{Bending parallel to the grain} &= 2.0 \times 5.7 \text{ N/mm}^2 \times K7 \\
&\quad \text{(depth factor)} \\
&= 11.4 \text{ N/mm}^2 \times K7 \\
\text{Tension parallel to the grain} &= 2.0 \times 3.4 \text{ N/mm}^2 \times K14 \\
&\quad \text{(width factor)} \\
&= 6.8 \text{ N/mm}^2 \times K14.
\end{aligned}
$$

The load capacity is determined using section 5.8 (BS 5268: Pt 2, (clause 16.3))

## 11.13 Design example 4: The cover required for metal fasteners

*Metal fasteners are to be used to secure SC4 timber members. Determine the amount of cover required to give 30 minutes fire protection.*

**165**

As the timber is SC4, the 30 minutes charring rate given in Table 11.1 is 20 mm. The metal fasteners must be either embedded within the residual section, which starts 20 mm below the surface of the timber, with any holes fully and securely plugged, or at least 20 mm of the same SC4 timber must securely cover the exposed part of the fastener.

If the SC4 timber members are used in trussed rafter construction, there are no fire resistance requirements and the metal fasteners can be used without restriction.

# 12 Chipboard

## 12.1 Introduction

Section 9 of BS 5268: Pt 2 applies to the structural use of type C5 wood chipboard that complies with BS 5669. Type C5 wood chipboard can only be used in dry exposure conditions where dry stress values apply. C5 wood chipboard must not be used structurally in continuously wet or immersed conditions.

Chipboard must be maintained in a first class condition prior to use as specified in BS 5669. The dimensional movements due to changing relative humidity must be provided for in the design, again as specified in BS 5669.

## 12.2 Durability

The use of type C5 chipboard is restricted to dry exposure conditions. Chipboard will lose strength, lose stiffness and become susceptible to fungal attack if subjected to high humidity or prolonged wetting.

## 12.3 Dimensions and section properties

Table 91b of BS 5268: Pt 2 gives the section properties of sanded chipboard of nominal thickness 6 mm to 40 mm, based on the minimum thickness tolerance permitted by BS 5669. For chipboard thicknesses not given in Table 91b and for unsanded boards, the section properties are based on the minimum thickness, which is found by subtracting the maximum negative tolerance shown in Table 12.1, from the quoted nominal thickness.

**Table 12.1   Maximum negative tolerance**

| Board type | Nominal thickness | Tolerance (mm) |
|---|---|---|
| Sanded | 6 mm to 25 mm | 0.4 |
|  | 26 mm to 40 mm | 0.5 |
| Unsanded | 6 mm to 25 mm | 0.8 |
|  | 26 mm to 40 mm | 1.0 |

## 12.4   Grades and marking

The grade stresses only apply to type C5 boards marked in accordance with and complying with BS 5669.

## 12.5   Grade stresses

The grade stresses given in Table 91c of BS 5268: Pt 2 apply to the long-term loading in the dry exposure condition and must be used in conjunction with the corresponding section properties given in Table 91b. It is assumed that all perimeter edges are either fully supported and/or have glued edge joints with adjacent boards.

## 12.6   Concentrated load capacity

Table 91d of BS 5268: Pt 2 gives the concentrated load capacity for type C5 wood chipboard for circular loaded areas of diameter 25 mm and 50 mm. The table can also be used for other shapes, by using the other shapes' smallest dimension as the diameter of the circular area. Interpolation can be used for loaded areas between 25 mm and 50 mm diameter. Loaded areas of less than 25 mm, must be increased to at least 25 mm by means of rigid plates. For floors, the concentrated load is assumed to be a point load, but for roofs it is assumed to act over an area of 300 mm × 300 mm.

Where concentrated loading perpendicular to the plane of the board is applied, it is necessary to ensure the permissible bending stress and permissible deflection is not exceeded due to the various load combinations. The effective board width is assumed to be the same as the effective span.

## 12.7 Duration of load

The grade stresses given in Table 91c of BS 5268: Pt 2 and the concentrated load capacities given in Table 91d of BS 5268: Pt 2 are modified by the duration of load factor $K81$ as given in Table 2.1. $K81$ is not applied to the bearing stress, the duration of load modification factor $K3$ is used instead. The bearing stress must be checked for each value of $K3$.

Load duration plays a considerable part in the calculations related to chipboard, and Table 91f of BS 5268: Pt 2 gives the modification factors $K82$, $K83$ and $K84$, that must be applied to the moduli of elasticity for the net long-term loads, the net medium-term loads and the net short- or very short-term loads, respectively. The net loads are the loads of the duration stated, excluding all other loads of longer duration. For example, the net very short-term load would be the wind load only.

In determining the deflections or deformations of the structural members, which are subjected to a combination of loads of different durations, each load duration category must be considered as acting separately and the deflections induced calculated separately. The total deflection is the sum of the deflections caused by the individual loads. The values of the elastic moduli are determined for each load duration category by multiplying the elastic moduli given in Table 91c by the appropriate modification factor from Table 91f.

## 12.8 Wood chipboard flexural members

In determining the total deflection, the shear and bending deflection must be considered, together with the addition of the deflections caused separately by the long-term, net medium-term and the net short- or very short-term loads appropriate to the member.

The permissible stresses for bending about either of the axes in the plane of the board, are the dry grade stresses given in Table 91c modified in accordance with $K81$ as given in Table 2.1 (Table 91e). When bending is not about either of the axes in the plane of the board, but is about the axis perpendicular to the plane of the board, if for example, edge-loaded as in a built-up beam, the tensile and compressive stresses induced by the bending compressive stresses are still those of Table 91c.

Rolling shear in stressed skin panels, box-beams and I-beams need only be considered at the contact area between the framing members and the chipboard. The grade rolling shear given in Table 91c must be multiplied by the stress concentration modification factor $K37 = 0.5$.

The lateral stability conditions of sections 3.11 and 3.13 also apply. A design example using chipboard is given in section 3.27.

# Index